MY LIFE IS WORTH LIVING!

MY LIFE IS WORTH LIVING!

Carol M. Creasey

UNITED WRITERS
Cornwall

UNITED WRITERS PUBLICATIONS LTD
Ailsa, Castle Gate, Penzance, Cornwall.

British Library Cataloguing in Publication Data

A catalogue record for this book is
available from the British Library.

ISBN 1 85200 051 1

Printed in Great Britain by
United Writers Publications Ltd
Cornwall

This book is dedicated to my husband John,
without whom I could not have coped.
Also acknowledgements to my son Jimmy, and
daughters Anita and Andrea.
It was always a team effort! Last but far from
least, Philip himself.

Chapter One

Paul was born at 2.30 pm on a Saturday afternoon in June. He was not actually due for another two weeks, and I had been lucky. It was a wonderful pregnancy, no sickness like I had with my first two children. Neither was there excessive weariness, and I felt bright and cheerful. The only difference was that I felt a bit more bloated, and my ankles were a little swollen. The doctor was not too concerned about it. The weather was warm, and he gave me some pills to take, and suggested I raised my feet a little when I rested.

I was longing to see this baby that had spent the last eight and a half months inside my body, and I was impatient for the last two weeks to pass. I already had Joe, now aged five. He had been at school for a term, and I also had Annette, who was three, and went to playschool. My husband, Mark, said that he wanted a boy. He thought boys were fun, but it was patently obvious that Annette could wind him round her little finger.

This particular Saturday the children were going out with a friend and her two children to Brighton. She had kindly offered to take them, and I was planning to do a bit of leisurely shopping and maybe have a rest in the afternoon. It was a difficult task to sit for long with Annette around. She was such a live-wire, so I welcomed the break. Mark worked every Saturday. He was trying to earn some extra money so that we could have central heating put in our house.

After Mary had taken the children the house seemed so quiet. I got into the car and drove down to our local supermarket. I put the shopping in the trolley after spending time deliberating on the best value for money items I could find.

Like most young couples with young families, after the mortgage and the bills were paid there were also playschool fees, and the children were growing fast and clothes and shoes were frequently needed. If we wanted to go out we had to pay a baby-sitter, as our parents did not live that near, so usually we didn't bother that much. Anyway, I consoled myself, with junior on the way I was really a bit tired in the evenings these days, if indeed Mark would be in from work, as he often worked later in the evening too. He was a telephone repair engineer and there was a glut of work after 5 pm.

As I ambled up to the check-out, I was relieved to find Tom, the Saturday boy, smiling at me, and ready to pack my bag. That meant he would carry it out to the car without the necessity of me having to request this service. I hated it when the cashier rang the bell and called for a 'carry-out' on her microphone. I imagined everyone was looking to see this woman who couldn't manage her own shopping. I hoped my size and shape would excuse me. The bill, as always, was more than I had meant to spend. As I looked at all the carrier bags full to the brim with food, I asked myself who ate it all, and I knew the answer too. We all did!

Tom was a cheerful lad. He loaded my bags into the car, and I thanked him. All I had to do was to get them out at the other end. Perhaps Mark would be home by lunch-time and he could help me. He had told me not to go shopping on my own now, but I had to. If he was at work how could he help me?

I arrived home at midday and Mark wasn't there. However, I was really 'lucky' because Kathy, our next door neighbour, was weeding her front garden. I say lucky with mixed feelings. She never stopped talking, and always wanted to be involved in everything. She was good hearted enough, but sometimes a bit overpowering. I think she was bored with being at home all day. Her husband was a company executive and seemed to jet all over the world to business meetings, but she never seemed to go with him. She helped me with the bags, taking all the heavy ones, chiding me at the same time for buying heavy goods on my own. I grinned and offered her a coffee, which I knew would be accepted. She made it whilst I unpacked the food. I was feeling very hungry now, and judging by the rolling discomfort in my stomach, so was junior!

I had a terrible craving for sausages, so I put some under the grill (a little less fat than fried!) and offered some to Kathy. She, of course, refused, and I was treated to the full details of how many calories a day she was allowed on her weight watchers diet, and descriptions of the food she did eat, and how much weight she was losing. Glancing at her ample frame I wondered how much of it was true. At least my bulge was only temporary! By now my sausages were cooked, and I put them between two slices of brown bread, resisting the urge to put butter on it, and gently spread mustard on top. I carried on eating whilst Kathy carried on talking. The speed of the onslaught of her verbal attack was anough to give anyone indigestion! However, I had developed the art of letting my mind wander on to other things, and although I looked at her and watched her lips moving, I was secretly wondering how long it would be before I could take a rest and she would go home. We were sitting in the lounge and, as her chair was near to the window, she spotted a figure going up her drive.

"Oh! That must be my washing-machine repair man. My programmer has gone. Sorry Carrie, must dash!" she said, getting up hurriedly. "Now remember, take a rest before the children come home!"

I nodded assent as she went out of the door. How fortunate! Now I could! Without that timely interruption she would have spent the rest of the afternoon telling me I should rest more.

It was a warm day, and as the time was now past midday the sun was getting really hot and the air felt humid, which I found made me even more tired. I left Mark a note telling him that I was in bed resting and I had left him a salad in the fridge.

I laid on top of the bed and raised my feet on the pillow as the doctor had told me to. I felt tired. The children had been so excited about their day out that they had woken me up at 6 am, and now it had caught up with me. I drifted off into a hazy sleep.

I woke up with a start, a feeling of discomfort inside. Those sausages must have given me indigestion! I thought ruefully. Serve me right for having them! I glanced at the clock, and it was showing 1 pm. I had only slept for about half an hour. I got out of bed, wondering where Mark was, and then I felt another pain. I hoped I wasn't going to be sick. I'd kept so well so far, but I did feel strange. I picked up the telephone to ring our doctor. Something wasn't right and I didn't like being alone. I had forgotten that it was Saturday, of course, and there was a rota system. Our doctor was not there, but a recorded message told me that if I left my number I would be rung back in a few minutes. This indigestion was getting more acute, so I decided to telephone the hospital to see if I could speak to the doctor I had seen at the antenatal clinic.

The hospital staff were very good. When I explained my problem they paged the doctor, who, as luck would have it, was around and free. He listened patiently whilst I explained I was alone and the surgery was not open.

"Well, Mrs Benson, the best thing is, if you feel well enough, to come up to out-patients, ask for me, and I will give you something for the discomfort."

"Thank you so much! Yes, I can drive up. It only takes five minutes." I put down the telephone, slipped on my comfortable shoes for driving, and made my way to the car. Then I remembered the note I had left for Mark. I went back and added a postscript. 'Have gone to see the doctor at the hospital. Back soon.'

I got into the car and drove slowly towards the general hospital. The discomfort had subsided now, and I felt a bit of a fraud. Oh well, Dr Meredith will check me over, anyway. I don't want to start getting indigestion in the night, I need my sleep even more now! I turned in at the hospital gates, and found the visitors car park. I idly glanced at my watch as I parked the car, 1.15 pm. It was still very hot, and I was glad to see a free space under the shade of a tree. I wound the window up and locked the door, and then walked with slow deliberate steps into the out-patients department. I went up to the desk as Dr Meredith had told me to, smiling at the receptionist. She looked a little ruffled. There was quite a crowd of people waiting for various reasons, and a man could be clearly heard berating the National Health system to his companion sitting on the chair next to him.

I explained that Dr Meredith was expecting me, and she smiled with relief.

"He's expecting you in room 3. Go in, get undressed, and put on a white gown."

I thanked her, and walked along the corridor to room 3. I got undressed and wrapped the voluminous gown around me. Even at eight months and two weeks it was too big! I sat on the chair and I felt another feeling of discomfort. I was glad I had come. After about five minutes Dr Meredith came in and smiled.

"I'm sure all is well, but let's take a look. Climb up on the bed." He used his arm to help me, and I felt like an elephant getting on the bed. His hand gently slid over my tummy and I gasped as another indigestion pain caught me, rolling with unexpected force around my stomach. He stiffened. "I'm just going to examine the cervix. How long have you been having these pains?"

"Only about forty-five minutes, they come and go. I had sausages for lunch," I volunteered.

"On no!" His voice quickened. "Indigestion, my foot! You're in labour!"

I heard the emergency bell ring. He had obviously pressed the button.

"But it's not like the labour pains I had before, it doesn't hurt much. It just feels like indigestion!"

He didn't appear to hear me, and a trolley appeared, pushed by two breathless nurses.

"Please take Mrs Benson down to the delivery room, fast!"

"But I haven't had an enema or been shaved," I protested. This was all too fast for me!

"No time for that! You're almost fully dilated!"

The shock hit me. I was giving birth!

Suddenly I knew it was true. I felt my waters break.

11

Chapter Two

I was lifted onto the trolley and taken at high speed along the corridor. Now I felt an overwhelming desire to push. I panted, "It's coming, I must push!"

"No! Hold on, you'll tear yourself . . . wait!"

Everything became a blur. I felt unreal.

I knew we had reached somewhere and I had been lifted onto another bed, but the faces were hazy. The pain was intense and now taking over my senses.

"OK get working now! Push!"

I pushed, and the feeling that the whole of my inside had a very hard object that needed to be expelled was strong, I remembered it from my other two births. That moment of indescribable pain! I felt it so intense, it racked at my insides, and then I must have briefly passed out. I could hear voices as though from the end of a long tunnel.

"I've given her a shot of Pethidine. Poor lady didn't even know she was in labour! — Come on again, Mrs Benson, push gently."

I tried to control my feeling of floating, and I vaguely felt the object move. My god it was like shucking peas!

"One more push, you're doing well! Your baby has lovely blond hair."

I came back to reality. Yes it was a baby I was having. It was ready to come now, not in two weeks! One more push and I felt it slither out of me, into welcome waiting arms, and I experienced a temporary relief from pain.

"Well done! You have a beautiful baby boy."

I heard his cry, it was like magic, and tears of relief pricked my eyes.

"Is he OK?" the question I'm sure all mothers ask.

"He looks perfect, but doctor will take a look at him as he was born rather quickly."

She held him gently and spoke softly. "My goodness little one, you were in a hurry to be born! Your mum was lucky!"

I realised that was the midwife talking. She wrapped him in a baby blanket and gave him to me. I looked at the downy blond hair, still covered in blood and discharge, and the very blue eyes that stared back at me. I felt a strong rush of maternal love for this helpless little being. After a couple of minutes I handed him back to be cleaned up whilst they helped me to deliver the afterbirth.

The nurse who was cleaning him enquired of the midwife, "Do you think we should put him in an incubator? It must have been a shock for him being born so quickly!"

As if to confirm her words he was crying, but I think it was more because the midwife had put him on the scales.

"What rubbish!" she replied. "You can't put a 6lb 14oz baby in an incubator. He's OK!"

I remember thinking that he probably wanted to be taken off those scales and be allowed to sleep off the effort involved in coming into the world, and then I felt the afterbirth slithering out of me.

"Looks like a nice healthy piece of steak," said a voice. "You have done well! You don't even need stitches!"

I heard a voice say, "Mr Benson is outside. He looks very white. Can he come in?"

I remembered my hurried note. Poor Mark! He wouldn't have understood. "Please let me see him, he wanted another son!"

My poor husband came in, obviously very shaken but relief in his face was apparent when he saw me smiling, and his new son could be heard lustily airing his lungs.

"I came home and found your note. I wondered what was wrong. I wouldn't have worked if I'd known this was going to happen! Who brought you here?"

"I drove myself."

"What! Carrie, you are silly!"

I hung my head, but the midwife intervened, laughing, "Your wife didn't know she was in labour. She had a very easy time in comparison to some labours."

Yes I knew that was true. Annette had taken three days from the onset of the labour pains, and this had been a doddle. The reality of the situation struck me. How easily I could have started to deliver whilst I was driving, and how dangerous it could have been. I explained to Mark, "I thought I was only coming up to get some pills for indigestion. The doctor was only checking me over. I'm relieved that our little one was born OK. Are we still calling him Paul?"

Mark thought for a moment. "Yes, we both agreed we liked it. What time is Mary bringing Joe and Annette back?"

I thought of how surprised they would be when they heard the news. "About 6 pm, I think. They'll be so excited when you tell them!"

"Well done, Carrie, for producing another son. That's great!" Now that the anxiety had lifted, Mark was elated. The nurse was hovering near my bed.

"Well, Mr Benson, I think your wife will be taken back to a ward now all the excitement is over. She will probably need to rest now."

I realised, in spite of my bubbling exterior, that my body felt physically very weary. Even a short labour takes it out of you. Mark kissed me good-bye, promising to return in the evening.

"Oh! Don't forget to 'phone both mums!"

"I won't," he promised.

"They may want to come this evening," I added. To me, the evening seemed a long way away. I was elated that our son was here, longing to show him to Joe and Annette, but now I wanted to sleep.

I was wheeled back into a ward, but put down the far end, away from the other mothers, who were already up and about. I remember the curtains being drawn, and then I must have slept for about three hours. I woke up to see a nurse drawing the curtains.

"Are you ready for a cup of tea?"

"Yes! My throat feels very dry actually."

"That's not very surprising. You lost a lot of fluid and now your body needs to take some in. When you've had your tea it will be time for the six o'clock feed. Are you breast-feeding?"

"I hope so." I smiled. "I did with my other two and they're rudely healthy!"

"Good girl! He will not get much from you other than colostrum at the moment, but that helps to clear his little bowels out. There's usually still mucous left after the birth."

She handed me a cup of tea, and it tasted like nectar to a dry throat.

"Dr Meredith wants a quick word."

"Oh! What about?"

She did not have time to answer as he appeared at that moment. "Well, Mrs Benson, your new son is doing well. I've given him a reflex test and he passed with flying colours, but there is one small problem."

The dismay must have shown in my face. I didn't want anything to spoil the happiness I was feeling right now.

"Don't worry, it's nothing serious. One of his testicles is undescended, not uncommon in newly born boys. Usually it rights itself without any help from us, if not we would wait until he was about five years old."

I had heard of this before, but it just put a slight shadow over things for me. Nothing can ever be perfect I reasoned with myself. "Thank you, doctor, for all your help. It's nice to know the hasty birth didn't cause him any problems."

"You should be able to take him home tomorrow, as long as you rest at home. How are my other two protégées?"

Dr Meredith had delivered Joe and Annette, indeed it was thanks to him that Annette had survived. I had been in labour for three days. I never really knew what went wrong, but I had been on a glucose drip because I'd been so sick, and at one point her heart beat had become weak. Eventually in desperation they had induced me, and she was safely born. She had thrived ever since and was now a bright, lively three-year-old, unable to keep still for a moment.

"They're fine, thank you. I know they'll love their new brother!"

He smiled and was gone, a very popular doctor, who also took great care of his mothers. I had heard that he had four children of his own, all under ten years old.

The nurse returned, wheeling the cot with my new son in.

I looked down, marvelling at the delicate features and tiny fingers waving out from under the blanket. He was hungry and letting us know it.

"Look at this little buster. He wants his mum!"

She picked him up and handed him carefully to me, wrapped in the cotton sheet.

"Next time you feed him you can get up and sit in a chair, but this time you must stay in bed in case you feel dizzy."

I leaned back against the pillows, holding his little warm body close to me. When I held him to my breast I felt the hardening of liquid, a momentary pain, and then the flow was released. Whatever it was, milk or colostrum, it seemed to satisfy him. He sucked eagerly and briefly opened his eyes, deep blue in colour I noticed. After a while I held him up to wind him and he then decided to go back to sleep. I gently patted his back and eventually he rewarded me with a loud burp.

Chapter Three

Visiting time had started and Mark arrived with Annette clutching his hand, and doing her best not to get too noisy in her excitement. Joe, who was always quieter, walked at his father's side. When they saw me all self-control disappeared. They both scampered up to the bed. "Hello, Mum, where's Paul?"

Then they spotted his cot at the end of the bed, and stood there with wide-eyed amazement. "Why are his eyes closed? Is he asleep? When will he wake up?"

"Can he play marbles with me?"

"Not yet, Joe, but he'll soon be old enough to. Babies grow up very fast. Do you remember when you used to show Annette your cars, and then one day she held one?"

Joe did remember! Nowadays, at the age of three, Annette loved to wind him up by hiding his cars, his favourite toys. He would spend hours lining them up and using his imagination, and when she disrupted his games it caused many arguments. So far she hadn't bothered with the marbles. She seemed to enjoy playing with them, rolling them to and fro for him, and I tried to encourage him to let her play, even if she didn't know how to play the game properly.

I think they were a little disappointed and it was an anticlimax, after all the excitement, just to see him lying there asleep like a little doll. I asked them about their day at Brighton.

"We went in the water and made sand-castles."

"You found sand at Brighton?" laughed Mark.

"Yes, Aunty Mary did!"

Annette was at the age when adults were all powerful,

17

and of course, if they wanted sand her faith in her Aunty Mary was unshaken because she had managed to provide it.

"Nannie's outside, she's got our flowers and hers' too, 'cos Daddy couldn't carry them and hold our hands."

"Oh, Annette, it was a secret!"

Joe was just about old enough to keep one, and he let her know it.

"Ssh, you two, never mind! Now you've seen Paul we'll go and sit in the car and let Nannie come in." He turned his face towards me, adding. "My mum and dad may pop in briefly too. They were all delighted when I 'phoned them, but so surprised that it was all over with so quickly."

"I'm still surprised myself, but it's lovely not to have to go those last two weeks!"

They all kissed me and I told them they could kiss their sleeping brother. Mark threw a look of pride at his new son, and I reminded them, "Be good for Nannie, and go to bed when you are told. I shall be home tomorrow, and then you can both help me with baby Paul."

Within about two minutes my mother popped in, armed with two bouquets of flowers.

"Well done, darling! Are you all right?"

She didn't wait for my reply, but rushed on, "Oh my goodness! He's just like your brother was at that age. His nose is the same, and the blond hair. The flowers are from Dad and I, and Mark got those for you."

Mark was not a man to buy flowers and I'm sure Mum was only too glad to relieve him of them. The message was short, 'Well done! Love Mark, Joe and Annette.'

Mum continued chatting and then called for a nurse to find some vases, which she hurried off to do. "It's a pity he's asleep. Still, I shall see him properly tomorrow."

We had already arranged for Mum to come and stay for the first week until I got back on my feet. The children would be looked after by her and this meant that Mark would not need to take time off. He was saving some days so that we could have a holiday a bit later on.

The children loved my mum, and I turned a blind eye to the fact that she spoilt them a little. They were fond of

Mark's mum too, but not in quite the same way. I knew there was a little bit of jealousy between the two mums and I tried to discourage it.

"Has Mark's mum been in to see you yet?"

"No, she may come a bit later."

I knew it would be important to Mum to be the first Grandma to see Paul, and her pleased expression confirmed this.

"Dad brought me here. He's parking the car."

As she spoke the door opened wide to admit my father. He kissed my cheek and duly admired his new grandson. I knew he would not stay for long, as he always felt very uncomfortable in hospitals. He satisfied himself that I was all right, and when I saw him looking fidgety I took my cue.

"Dad, you ought to go home and water the garden. It's been a hot day."

The relief on his face was apparent. "Are you sure? Mum is going back with Mark, I know, but I don't want those roses to die!"

"Of course, you go. You've seen Paul and it's only women's talk. We'll bore you." I smiled as he kissed me good-bye.

"My gorgeous daughter. You still are you know!"

My dad had always made a lot of fuss of me. Mum had been the stricter one, and he would have spoilt me more if she hadn't seen that I was disciplined when it was needed. She wasn't like that with Joe and Annette though. She felt, as their Nannie, it was her prerogative to spoil them.

After Dad had gone Mum checked again with me what time Joe needed to be at school, and also Annette at play-school. Luckily both places were within walking distance of one another, which was useful as Mum had never learnt to drive.

"I'll go and sit with Joe and Annette so that Mark can come in again. He didn't stay long!" she informed me.

"I do appreciate your consideration, Mum," I replied. "I hope the kids don't jump over you too much in the car."

She laughed. "They're no different to how you were."

I grinned. I knew I had been a handful!

"Bye, see you tomorrow, and sleep well." She gave me a hug, another beaming proud look at the still sleeping Paul,

19

and disappeared out of the door. Within a few minutes Mark was back.

"Are the kids OK?" I enquired.

"Yes, your mum's given them some sweets and is playing I-Spy with them. I wonder when my mum's coming! She was waiting for Dad to come in to bring her."

I often counted my blessings as far as family relationships were concerned. I was pretty lucky with my in-laws. After some of the stories of family discord and unpleasantness, Mary made me realise that mine were, all things being considered, very nice. True there was a little rivalry between the families, but nothing that could not be handled. He smiled when he saw the flowers in water. "Your mum wanted to bring them in. I didn't stop her."

"That's OK, they're lovely! Thanks darling. I hope I can bring them when I come home."

We continued to talk about everyday events and make plans for when I was back on my feet again. A little later Mark glanced at his watch, nervously, "Seven-fifty, only ten minutes of visiting time left!"

As if in answer to his comment the door opened tentatively, "Here she is, Mark's here too!"

In came Mark's parents, beaming.

"We came right through the ward looking for you, not realising you were down this end," explained his mother, and then she paused when she saw Paul. "Oh, there he is!" She said, wonderingly. "Isn't he like Joe and his dad, of course!"

Everyone looked at babies in their own way, and saw a likeness to someone in their own family. I felt that Paul was Paul. Yes, he was like Joe and Annette were at his age, but I also knew he could change his looks as he grew. He stirred in his sleep and his eyes, the deep blue colour briefly illuminated, flickered open, much to my mother-in-law's delight.

"I hope we're not disturbing him," she said anxiously. I knew that newborn babies were oblivious to everything but their own needs, but she was showing grandmotherly concern.

"No, of course not. When the visiting time ends the nurse will be taking him back to the nursery for the night."

20

I was grateful for that. Once home, of course, I would expect to be up every night feeding him for a while.

Susan, my mother-in-law, wanted to hear the details of my 'indigestion' labour, and I told her about it, watching the reaction of surprise on her face.

"Not at all like Annette's labour," was her comment.

"No, thank goodness! Hopefully this is a sign of an easy baby to cope with after such an easy birth."

Susan looked doubtful, "It doesn't always follow!"

"I know, Mum, I was only joking!"

The bell for the end of visiting time went, and this was the cue for Mark and his parents to go.

Chapter Four

I was allowed to go home on Sunday afternoon. Paul was a hungry baby and he seemed to catch on to breast-feeding very quickly. He had a lusty appetite and a strong suck, and already my milk was coming through. I put a white sleep suit on him, and as the weather was still very warm, I wrapped a light cotton blanket around him, binding his arms inside to make him feel secure. He seemed a good baby so far, only waking to be fed, and at the moment totally egocentric as newborn babies are. Except at feed time, the world around him just did not appear to exist. When I fed him his vivid blue eyes stared at me, but as yet there was no response to my smile, or any flicker of recognition.

Mark arrived in the car and I put the sleeping Paul into his carrycot, after being given a send-off by the nurses. The tradition was that one of them would carry the newly born infant to the car, whilst the mother walked.

I thanked them for all their kindness. I had already given one of my bouquets to another mother, who, sadly didn't seem to have many visitors, and the one from Mark was going home with me.

When we arrived home Joe and Annette were waiting. I didn't want them to feel jealous, so I made sure my arms were free to hug them whilst Mark brought the carrycot in and carefully put it down.

"Joe, Mum would love a cup of tea."

He had just learnt to do this on his own, with a little adult supervision, so he willingly trotted off to do it for me. Annette climbed onto my lap. She was still hardly more than a baby, after all, and in spite of all her lively ways, was

22

vulnerable enough to feel insecure. I cuddled her whilst I drank my tea and promised both the children that they could see Paul have his feed at six o'clock. They had been fascinated to learn that Paul's milk would be coming from me and not from a bottle, so this seemed a good way to educate them.

"Mummy's going to have a rest now. She needs to rest to get herself back on her feet to look after you all," said Mark.

"That's why Nannie's here to look after you," I explained. My mother had busied herself putting out a line full of washing.

I went to bed and Paul slumbered in his carrycot next to me. So far I was lucky with him. I remember Joe used to wake up just as I fell asleep. He seemed to have a lot of wind. I used to worry about him when he screamed, but when I took him to the doctor he had advised me to take my time when winding him and buy a bottle of gripe-water. Annette had been less fretful. Well, she had to compensate for her traumatic entry into the world! So far Paul was easy too. I fell into an uninterrupted sleep, which lasted right up until the next feed time.

This was to be the pattern of events for the next six weeks. We settled into a comfortable routine. Paul slept literally from one feed to the next, and only cried when he was hungry. Joe and Annette helped in their own way, fetching nappies, helping to change him and wind him, and I was pleased to let them be involved. I was impatiently waiting for the day when he would start to smile at us, his family, and I knew that Mark would be looking forward to his first responses. On the occasions when Paul did look at me, his very vivid blue eyes seemed to have a faraway look in them, which I hadn't noticed with Joe and Annette. He was a beautiful baby to look at, with his fair skin, very blond hair and his almost violet blue eyes, and people frequently stopped to admire him in the pram. After about the first month he started to wake up a little before he was hungry. He also stayed awake longer after feeds. One thing puzzled me, instead of crying for attention, if I picked him up to spend a few minutes playing with him, or cuddling him before a feed, he would start to cry. He would only stop if

I put him down again. I suppose, because it was early days after the birth and I was sensitive at this time, I felt rejected. He still had contact with me for breast-feeding, and he was doing fine and putting on weight, so I dismissed my fears as irrational. However, the feeling that he didn't want me to show him any affection persisted, and this took the edge off my happiness. I knew it was wrong to compare children, but as Joe had always been a clinging baby and always seemed to like being cuddled and played with when awake, and Annette, too, had never wanted to just lay in her pram when awake, I found Paul's acceptance of this, and his protest at human contact other than for feeding, strange! I told Mark and he laughed and said I should be glad that Paul wasn't a demanding baby. After all, with three children now, how would I find time to cope?

Six weeks almost to the day after Paul was born, when I was putting him to bed that night, I noticed a tiny pink mark under his eye, almost like a strawberry mark. At first I thought that he had scratched himself and it was not significant.

That night sticks vividly in my mind, although it was twenty-one years ago. It was to be a night I would never forget!

Chapter Five

The children were in bed, asleep, and I had prepared a salad for us. We usually ate dinner in the evening because Mark worked on most Saturdays, and took sandwiches with him during the day. He had arrived home at about four o'clock, in time to spend a little time with the children. I popped out to get some shopping whilst he gave them their tea, and they all watched a bit of television. Now that my family had increased to three children I didn't like to prevail on friends. Not only that, Saturday was a day when most husbands were at home, and I thought it was unfair to ask anyone to have them in case it disrupted their family routine.

We sat down to eat, the chicken salad was nice and I had a plateful of it. I had also made a fruit salad and we had this with ice-cream afterwards. The house seemed still and quiet, and once again I thought how lucky we were to have three children so young, all asleep by eight o'clock, and the rest of the evening to ourselves. After we had eaten we looked through a well thumbed Butlin's brochure and decided we would book a week's holiday with them if we could. It seemed a sensible place to go with a young family. All amenities were laid on, including facilities for babies, and also there were no problems if the weather was bad.

Paul had now cut out his middle of the night feed and his last one was usually at about ten-thirty. He was then able to last round until about six-thirty in the morning, which fitted in nicely with my schedule, as it left me free by seven-thirty to get Joe and Annette up. I could hear Paul snuffling and making preliminary noises to let me know that his feed time was approaching. I lifted him out of his cot carefully and sat

b

in my comfortable chair to feed him whilst Mark watched a film on television. He fed well although he was sleepy, and after he had brought his wind up he drifted back to sleep, his little head resting against my arm. His soft, warm little body stirred my maternal emotions and I felt a wave of love run through me. Babies were so vulnerable, so utterly dependent on us for their survival! I carefully changed his nappy, trying not to disturb him, and made him comfortable for the night. Mark glanced over, "Good night, little buster, sleep tight!"

I clutched Paul to me, enjoying the warm feel of his little head on my arm, and walked slowly to his carrycot. As I put him in there I kissed the soft little cheek and suddenly he woke up! He gave an angry yell, flaying out his arms in annoyance, as if to fight off the unwelcome intrusion. I felt the tears prick my eyelids as I felt the rebuff of my show of affection. Mark was amazed to see me suddenly dissolve into tears, but I found I couldn't help it, even though it seemed such a minor thing. "I don't think he likes me! He cries when I cuddle him. The others weren't like him!"

He put his arm round me, comfortingly, and we both looked at the now sleeping baby.

"Give him time. Maybe he'll grow up to be a boy who doesn't like sloppiness. Of course he loves you! He just doesn't understand yet about kisses and cuddles."

Feeling a bit more reassured I drew Mark's attention to the red mark under Paul's eye.

"He's probably caught himself with his little fingernails. It'll heal up in a few days, but we'll keep an eye on it." Then seeing that I was in a low frame of mind, Mark took the carry-cot upstairs. When he came down again he said, "I've put him in the other bedroom. He doesn't wake up in the middle of the night now."

"Yes, you're right." It suddenly struck me that maybe Mark felt a little bit left out with such a young family taking up a lot of my attention most of the time. I freed my thoughts away from children and we sat down together to fill out our booking form for the holiday. At about 11.30 we decided to go to bed and we settled down for a peaceful night's sleep.

26

I woke up some hours later with a pain that I can only describe as agony. I dragged myself out of bed because after all the fruit and salad I thought I might need the toilet. The whole of my inside felt as though it was rending open with this terrible pain! Everything was going black, and I could hear this dreadful screaming which was coming from deep inside me! I was aware of Mark's face and I vaguely heard him on the telephone. "Emergency, please! My wife is in terrible pain. Any doctor, just come and help her!"

The only way I could find to relieve the pain was to crouch on the floor, with my knees drawn up to my stomach, and I stayed like this until the doctor arrived, refusing all Mark's supplications to get back into bed. In the end I was aware of being covered with a duvet, but I was sweating, and still the pain racked my inside.

When the doctor arrived he didn't make me get on the bed. He looked at me quickly on the floor and I remember feeling the prick of an injection, which seemed to subdue the pain a little and make me feel sleepy.

"An ambulance to 1 Ifield Road, quickly please!" In aside to Mark, "I've given her a shot for the pain, but we need to move fast!"

"Doctor, will she be all right? What's happening?"

I struggled up on my elbow. I could feel the pain, but not so acutely, and I felt detached from it, and from them, but I managed to grasp the fact that I was going to hospital.

"The baby, I'm breast-feeding him! I can't leave him."

"That's OK, Mrs Benson. You are going to have your appendix out and you'll need all your strength after the operation, and probably your milk would dry up anyway. Just put him onto a bottle Mr Benson. If you cannot cope I'll arrange for the health visitor to come and she will fix you up with a home help for a few days."

How dare he make decisions for me! I thought.

"No! If I go to hospital Paul comes with me!" I protested fiercely. The thought of being parted from my baby had roused me from my foggy semi-conscious state of mind, and I reiterated, "If I can't take Paul, I'm not going."

Brave words, but the pain was rolling around again. I gripped my fingers against it. I could feel myself panting.

27

"OK, we musn't upset her, the ambulance is here. If her milk dries up the nurses will be able to help her feed him by bottle."

Mark was relieved. "Thank you, doctor. I just want to see her out of this pain! It's been awful watching her writhing on the floor and being so powerless. When will they operate?"

"Soon after she gets there. We don't take any chances when it's like this! If you visit her tomorrow after about midday she will be back in the ward, recovering." He corrected himself, "I mean today, later today, of course! I'm afraid at four o'clock in the morning I'm inclined to get my days confused." He spoke kindly to me, "You will soon feel much better, my dear, you are going to have your appendix out. It's very unfortunate right after a pregnancy, but you will cope."

I inclined my head towards Mark, I felt weary and helpless, and resigned to the surgeon's knife, anything to rid me of this pain. "Don't telephone our parents at this time of the morning, Mark. You will give them such a shock."

I had recovered enough to realise what a drama it would cause at four o'clock in the morning.

The men with the stretcher had arrived and came upstairs to get me. They greeted me cheerfully and proceeded to lift me onto the stretcher, whilst the doctor and Mark filled them in with the details.

I reminded them, "Don't forget my baby! He's in the carrycot in the room next door."

They didn't argue, as they took the stretcher down the stairs I was aware of the door of Joe and Annette's room opening, and two sleepy, bewildered figures stood there, looking at me in amazement.

"*Mummy!* Why are you on that stretcher? Where are you going?" Annette was crying and Mark was there to reassure them.

"Mummy has a bad tummy and she's going to hospital to be made better. We'll see her soon!"

"Oh Mummy! You're not having another baby again! Where will it sleep?" said the ever practical Joe.

In spite of my unfortunate predicament the funny side of this struck me, and my stretcher bearers too.

28

"God luv, he thinks you're a fast worker!" grinned one of the ambulance men. In spite of my pain I found myself chuckling with amusement.

Mark followed down with Joe and Annette to see me into the ambulance, and one of the men went back to bring Paul and his carrycot. He was blissfully asleep, which was just as well! The last thing that I remember was their anxious faces and Mark pressing my hand.

"I'll be along as soon as I can in the morning. Please be all right!"

I think they were kissing me good-bye, and then I must have drifted off to sleep.

Chapter Six

I woke up to see a nurse bending over me.

"Just going to give you a pre-med."

I felt the jab of a needle, and vaguely remember a trolley moving down a corridor. Then there was a figure in green, smiling and reassuring me that all would be fine. I heard, "She's just had a pregnancy. See the brown line where her stomach is. Let's hope the uterus has returned to normal. It's barely six weeks!"

I remember thinking that it should have done, because I had religiously been doing my post-natal exercises, and then everything became blurred and finally blank.

I woke up because I could hear a voice calling me from what seemed a long way away. It was a nurse. I felt confused. Had I just given birth? No! I remembered, I had a boy. But where was my baby?

"Nice to see you awake, Mrs Benson, a cup of tea is coming round."

I was suddenly aware that my throat felt very sore and my inside was hurting badly.

"Take care when you move, you have stitches."

I didn't wait for the tea, but pointed towards the jug of water on the bedside cabinet, and croaked for water.

She smiled sympathetically, "Yes, the sore throat will be better tomorrow. It's the anaesthetic."

I began to remember what had happened. "Where's my baby? I brought him with me!"

"Yes, he's at the foot of your bed, but you can't feed him until your milk flows again. The operation will temporarily dry it up until you start taking fluids. You certainly were unlucky, having a ruptured appendix straight after a pregnancy. I've never heard of that before!"

"My stomach really hurts, and I feel so weak!"

"Yes, of course, but you will get stronger soon, stick to light foods, and jelly and ice-cream will also help your throat."

I roused myself from my own self-pity to ask, "How has Paul been feeding?"

"Well, he had a bottle at 6.30," she said reluctantly, "but he brought some of it up, and he has been restless."

As if to confirm the truth of her words Paul started to wail and thrash his arms about. I knew he was hungry.

"What's the time?"

"Nearly 2.30. I will take him into a side ward and feed him. Your husband wants to come in now that you're awake."

With that she wheeled the cot out, and Paul's wails gradually died away.

I knew that I couldn't feed him yet, but I was determined to increase my intake of fluids to get my body working properly again. I drank two cups of tea and when Mark came in with the children I got them to get me a fresh jug of water. They had brought me a bottle of black currant and orange squash, and as Mark had been told that I would be in for at least ten days, there was also a bag of fruit for me to eat when I felt better. They didn't stay for long. I must have looked tired, and after they went I slept for the rest of the afternoon. When I woke up later for more tea, I made a point of drinking a pint of fruit squash and I was pleased to feel the familiar pricking of my breasts filling up, and their hardness confirmed this.

"I am going to feed Paul at 6.30," I informed the doctor who had come in to see me after the nurse had checked that my temperature and pulse were normal.

"Give yourself until tomorrow. A bottle won't harm him!" he advised.

"No! If I stop for any longer my milk will go. I want to do it now."

He looked at me, doubtfully. "It's up to you, of course, but I don't advise it."

31

Tough! I thought. I couldn't explain why I had such a feeling of well-being when I breast fed, but Joe and Annette had thrived on it, and it was important to me to give Paul the same chances. I was one of those lucky women who had lots of milk, and Joe and Annette had always been far more resilient to childhood illnesses than some of my friends' bottle fed babies. I owed it to him to give him the same start in life. The doctor could see it was important to me, indeed, otherwise why was Paul there with me? I got my way, and he was feeding from me at 6.30. Whilst I was feeding him, in came the nurse with a clean nappy.

"I'm so glad you're feeding him again. He brought up a lot of his last two feeds, and he's been fretting all day."

I knew that hunger would be about the only thing that would cause Paul to fret, so I wasn't surprised to find he quickly settled down again after I had fed him.

He was left by my bed. I think they knew I needed to have him near me for my own well-being. I had to feed him again at 10.30, and my milk seemed to be coming back well, although I still felt very weak and my stomach hurt when I tried to move around or sit up. I did not complain about this to anyone, which was just as well, as I had worse to follow! On the second day I had to suffer a very painful penicillin injection and this course of treatment continued for the next ten days! They told me that no chances were going to be taken with me, as apparently my appendix had been on the point of rupturing.

I battled on with the breast-feeding and somehow my milk returned properly. I felt pretty grotty for a few days, but my stomach was too sore for me to eat, although I kept having fluids and soup. Milk pudding, jelly and ice-cream became part of my diet. Gradually my throat improved and I felt stronger, and although my improvement was taking longer, as the doctor had predicted, because I was using my strength in making milk, I was rewarded by seeing that Paul had settled down again and was keeping his feeds down.

On the third day, the nurse, who was really friendly and chatty, noticed the mark under Paul's eye. She told me it was a birthmark. This puzzled me, because no one had noticed it when he was born. When I looked, I could see that

32

it was getting bigger. When the doctor came back to see me I asked him about it. He confessed that he wasn't a paediatrician, but advised me to see one when I went home. This made me feel depressed. This angry red blemish on Paul's face was rather near to his eye, and it marred his cute little face. I started to feel self-pity. Why did he have to have it? Why was I so unlucky to have needed an operation so soon after having him?

On the tenth day the doctor said I could go home, but I must try and get some rest when I could. My mother could not come over and help out because she worked and she already had taken her holiday when Paul was born. Mark, too, was running out of annual leave. We had booked our holiday for a month's time, the end of August, and because of my unfortunate circumstances the welfare officer attached to the hospital had arranged for a home help to come. She was to do some of my heavier house work and also keep an eye on the children, who were on holiday from school and playschool. It was hoped that I would be back on my feet by the time we went on holiday.

Chapter Seven

A couple of days after I had returned home from hospital, I took Paul to see our family doctor, to get advice about his birthmark. He told me it was called a naevus, and for the first year of his life it would grow with his face. I was horrified! He tried to reassure me that in time it would tone down and be less red and angry looking, but it hurt me very much to think that he could not verify that it would go completely. My self-pity was festering. Why should *my* son have an ugly birthmark?

The doctor gave me a letter to take with Paul to the paediatrician at the hospital. He explained that they would need to see him about once a month. As the mark was near to his eye they would want to check that it didn't grow upwards and block his sight. I was fast going down the road of self-pity and despair! Even the love of my family couldn't seem to lift me out of this depression. Little did I know my problems had hardly started! My holiday didn't really help, but I tried to put on a happy face for the sake of Joe and Annette.

By the time that Paul was three months old, his mark was pretty large, and I was finding it hard to cope with comments from other people when they saw him in his pram. My beautiful son was no longer perfect! He was still not sociable and spent longer alone in his pram, when awake, gurgling contentedly to himself, his eyes content to watch trees moving in the breeze, and other similar happenings in the garden. He still didn't smile and wasn't attempting to hold himself up when on my lap, in a preliminary attempt to sit up. I became convinced that there was something wrong with him, but no one would listen to me. It was assumed that I was suffering from post-natal depression. One morning I woke up and my milk had gone! It never returned. I had no choice but to change to a bottle, and although Paul accepted it more readily at four months because he had also started on solids, and did not vomit it back, within a week he had developed a rash. I took him to the doctor and he prescribed some cream to put on it. He told me, "Try changing his formula. He has infantile eczema, and he will be allergic to certain things. You will have to watch his diet."

At six months he developed a cough, which seemed particularly noticeable at night. Again we returned to the doctor. He told me that Paul was asthmatic and I was given two bottles of medicine to give to him three times a day. This disturbed me even more, as I had had a sister who had died before I was born from the effects of an asthma attack, and I had always hoped it would not be passed on to any of my children.

This was, also, the end of undisturbed nights, from then onwards Paul developed the habit of waking up, sometimes several times a night if he was wheezy, and if I was lucky, only once or twice. I became used to jumping out of bed and going to settle him before he could cough himself into an attack. I loved my little boy so much it grieved me to see these things happening to him, and I knew my mental attitude was wrong, but I just could not cope and I could see it affecting my family life. Although surrounded by my family, I felt alone!

His naevus continued to grow, but one day something happened to give me a glimmer of hope. Paul was laying in his pram, kicking and cooing to himself, watching the trees blowing in the wind. Although it was December the weather was mild and he enjoyed being in the garden, so I was still putting him out, well wrapped up in a pram suit.

I went outside to get him in for his lunch and to my amazement he looked at me and smiled a response for the first time ever!

It was wonderful to me! At the age of six months my son had smiled at me, and for the first time I felt he loved and needed me.

35

He was still very interested in food, but I was now learning that some foods upset him. He could not eat eggs. I gave him a boiled one once and it came back straight away. Now that he was taking solids his eczema was not quite so bad, but over the years I was to find that his skin would give adverse reaction to certain foods and their additives. It was very difficult to know, and each new introduction had to be done by trial and error.

Paul had gone through a very bad patch just after I had put him on the bottle when my milk dried up. He was, apparently, allergic to milk, and in a desperate bid to stop him from scratching his face to pieces I had to bind his hands in mittens. I was very unhappy about doing this, because I knew that without being able to use his hands to learn to hold things his development would be held up even more.

However, he was learning to cope, and so was I! He loved his bath and I had special emulsifying cream to put in the water to keep his skin from becoming even dryer, and I tried to make some time for him to have a long bath every evening before bed. Joe and Annette helped me, and although they were disappointed that he couldn't play with them yet, they always spoke to him and never gave up trying to attract his attention. They accepted his birthmark and had totally convinced themselves that it would disappear like magic when he was older. Their faith and conviction were heartening.

"We love him anyway. He's our brother!" I was told.

On this particular day after I had given Paul his lunch I freshened him up and put him in his pram. I had an appointment at the hospital in the afternoon, and luckily the hospital was within walking distance. It was a routine check on the naevus and I went through the usual procedure of having him checked by the paediatrician. I was relieved to hear that there was no immediate danger of it affecting his sight.

I carried on with the monthly appointments, but the paediatrician passed off my attempts to point out that Paul's development was very slow. I was told that acute eczema caused a temporary retarding of development. I did so hope that this was true!

Paul reached the age of nine months and apart from his

smiles, which were rare, he did not appear to have progressed much. When he was due for his monthly check up, which was always in the afternoon, I dressed him in his new blue pram outfit that Mum had bought for him, and I vowed to myself that today I would insist on having his development properly checked. "I owe it to you, my darling," I told him, fiercely holding back my tears as he gazed at me, wonderingly!

Although it was only March and early in the year, there was a gentle breeze and the sun was shining. As I walked along enjoying the air, and Paul peacefully slept, I wondered once again whether all my misgivings were wrong. After all, he did smile now, only at people he knew, it's true, but if he could find something to smile about with his difficulties then so should I. I was a fine example! I've often heard it said that babies all develop at different rates, and I knew that if he felt wretched with the effects of asthma and eczema, this could be the reason that his progress was being held up.

When I arrived at the hospital I made my way to the children's department and parked his pram just outside the doors. I scooped him into my arms and carried him inside to book in at the reception desk. I sat down to wait our turn, leaning him back against my arm. As he could not sit up I could not put him on the floor or in the play-pen full of toys that had been provided. So far Paul had shown no great interest in toys. He could hold a baby cup and drink from it, but whether that was instinct of survival taking over I couldn't be sure.

When it was our turn Dr Pearson, the lady paediatrician, checked his face and once again reassured me that the naevus was not impeding his sight. She said comfortingly, "It won't grow much more now. What has happened is that it has grown with his face. After about a year it will become less red and angry looking, and by the time he is at school it will have shrunk up considerably."

"That's a relief doctor! But I'm still concerned that he is not sitting up yet. He does smile a bit and I do realise that the eczema and asthma don't help."

"How old is he now? . . . Nine months – mm!"

Her face became thoughtful. She laid Paul on the bed and tried to hold his hands and let him try to pull himself up.

37

He resented the interference and protested loudly. She also tried laying him on his tummy, but all he succeeded in doing was burying his nose in the sheet and coughing. She gave him back to me. I walked over to the window so he could watch the branches of the tree moving in the gentle breeze, and this caused him to chuckle with merriment. She then asked me details of what he could and couldn't do. After she had finished writing it all down she rang the bell by her desk and explained that a nurse would come and take Paul for a nappy test.

"We can tell a lot from the results of a urine sample," she added.

The nurse came in and, after Dr Pearson had explained what was required, gently took Paul from me. He took little notice of her, but stared past her to see if there were any more trees to capture his attention. I felt both relief and fear that at last someone was beginning to realise that I could be right about Paul. He was not developing as he should. I was overcome with a strong need to know, whatever the cost to me emotionally.

"What are you testing him for? What do you think is wrong?"

Dr Pearson met my eyes reluctantly. "Paul is a very unusual looking baby. His head is an unusual shape, his skin is very fair, so is his hair, and his eyes are very blue!"

"I know all this, doctor, but he has our family colouring. What does it signify?"

She looked at me uncomfortably. "I shan't know the results of the test for about ten days, but I strongly believe that Paul is suffering from a very rare disease that causes the body to reject certain vitamins, even though he may be getting them in his daily diet. The result of this is retardation and a breakdown in health."

This sounded really frightening to me, but I had a strong desire to know.

"So what will happen? How can he be treated to put it right?"

"It cannot be put right. It is unlikely that Paul will live beyond five years old. I am really sorry, but it's best that you know."

38

I stared at her in amazement and disbelief. My ears must be deceiving me! She was telling me that my son was slowly dying! No! . . . No! . . . No!

I suddenly knew that I wanted him to live so much. My fierce maternal love fought against this terrible shock. Even if he was going to be retarded we all needed him. He was a part of our family. All I could say in response was, "I'll look after him in every way that I can, take care of him and love him, even if it's only for a few years."

I couldn't even cry or shout or scream. All the noise was going on inside me, but I couldn't let it out. Surely this was a nightmare! I prayed that I would wake up soon. I felt as if I had been given an injection. Everything seemed so far away. She was explaining that the disease had only recently been identified and she put a name to it, some long Latin word, but all I could think of was that it had happened to my son. I wanted to cry, or scream, or beat my hands against the desk! In spite of all this I remained passive. My emotions were in turmoil, but my body physically remained remote, numbed and shut off from these terrifying revelations.

How long I sat there like this whilst she spoke to me quietly and sympathetically I have no idea. I remember the nurse bringing Paul back from his nappy test. He had fallen asleep. I cuddled his soft little body up to me. I could not imagine life without him. He was part of our family. I hadn't carried him for all those months and given birth to him all for nothing. He must live! I willed him to live!

I cannot remember much about walking back from the hospital. Later I found my appointment card with a date for two weeks later, but I do not remember what I said or who I said it to. Everything else except my thoughts is a blank. The thing I do remember is that I had reached Jane's house. She was a close friend of mine with two sons of Joe and Annette's ages. We had met at playschool, and she had offered to have Annette whilst I took Paul for his appointment. She had heard me walking up the drive and opened the door with a welcoming smile on her face. This was replaced by a look of horror when suddenly all my self-control went. It snapped! The tears came like torrents. I could not stop sobbing. The thought that my son was living on borrowed time, and was

39

going to get worse and suffer, was more than I could bear! I somehow managed to choke out my story to her and I remember her voice, quietly doing her best to soothe me. Little Annette was there. She was crying too! Then I felt ashamed of myself, frightening my little girl and letting her see me at my lowest ebb. All the months of wondering and worrying had culminated in this outburst, and I was totally unable to control myself.

Chapter Eight

Somehow we got through the next two weeks. I tried to carry on as normal, and when I look back I wonder how we all coped. Joe and Annette knew now that something was wrong with Paul, but their love for him was totally unwavering. I tried not to let them see me upset. Sometimes it really got to me, and I would have outbursts of weeping, so I shut myself away in the bedroom. The worst thing, I thought, would be telling Mark. He didn't believe me. He thought that I had misunderstood, and patiently suggested that we wait for the result of the test.

The day that I went back for the result Mark came with me. This helped, to have someone else along, and we sat waiting in fearful trepidation to be called in to see Dr Pearson. Mark spoke first. "Well doctor, what have you got to tell us?" He was twisting his fingers nervously, I noticed.

Dr Pearson looked at her notes and cleared her throat. "Yes Mr and Mrs Benson, I am pleased to tell you that your son does not have the vitamin deficiency disease that I originally suspected."

I gazed at her in incredulous amazement. Were we getting a reprieve? Maybe God had not forsaken us after all!

Mark was not to be placated. "No! I thought you had got it wrong. Now tell me what right you had to give my wife news like that! You put us all through hell and misery for the last two weeks without even waiting for the results of the test!"

"I'm sorry, your wife pressed me to know, and all the symptoms seemed to point to this."

"I don't care, and I don't trust your medical theories any more!" he sneered. "We can do better ourselves."

"But Mr Benson! There is something wrong, and we need to find out what it is."

"You're not using *my* son as a guinea-pig just because you've discovered a new illness."

With that, Mark nudged my elbow authoritatively and quickly propelled me out of the room. I knew that he was right, but it was the way that he had done it. Paul still needed to be checked in his development, and also the growth of his naevus needed to be monitored. I could not go against him when I knew that he was defending me, so we both left the hospital with our heads held high, but no longer having Paul under the care of Dr Pearson.

Mark had now totally convinced himself that paediatricians were all incapable, and that Paul was a normal baby. As the months passed with very little change I realised that either he could not accept that there was a problem or he was trying to keep it from me. I did not dare ask, but it was almost as if he hoped that if he ignored it that it would go away. From then onwards, sadly, our marriage started to go downhill. Yes, we both loved our children, but we could not talk to each other about Paul's backwardness. I found it too painful because I was filled with guilt. I felt that I had let Mark down badly by producing a backward child! We became remote from one another. The one thing that should have bound us together pushed us apart. Dr Pearson had been right about one thing. After about a year, when Paul's face had grown quite full and chubby, his naevus gradually began to shrink. It had faded to a faint pink mark from the original angry red one before. In time it was hardly noticeable, seeming to blend in with his pink cheeks. At fifteen months he was still unable to sit up. I found I now had less friends. Mary had started to become unavailable to look after him, and her two children no longer came round to play with mine. I asked her why this was and she admitted it was because of Paul.

"He's odd! He takes no notice of anyone else, just sits in his baby chair, laughing at nothing. Sorry, Carrie, but doesn't it ever occur to you he could be mad. I don't want his habits to rub off on my two."

Her words cut into me like a knife, wounding me so deeply,

and I was filled with a great rage!

"How dare you, you bitch!" The words slipped out heedlessly. "Don't you know what handicapped means? He needs our help."

Strong words, and I made no apology for using them on my so-called friend. She shrugged her shoulders, unmoved.

Mary had been my friend ever since school days, almost twenty years. We had been married in the same year, and she had been my bridesmaid. Our friendship had survived arguments over friends and boyfriends, but I would not allow it to survive now! I did not want to know her any more and could not forgive her spiteful remarks. I lost other friends, too, but I certainly found out who my true ones were. The most loyal of them was Jane, and she helped me with Paul whenever she could. However, unfortunately for me, her husband was moved to Bristol with his company and they went there to live.

When Paul was eighteen months we went Christmas shopping to buy the children's presents. My mother-in-law, Susan, had offered to come over to our house and look after the children, give them lunch and stay until we got back. I needed the break! It was getting that I had to take Paul everywhere with me. He was heavy now and difficult to lift. My mother, much to her great disappointment, was now unable to help. Her health was failing. She had rheumatoid arthritis and her arms and legs, as well as being very painful, were getting too stiff for her to use properly. There was no way that she could lift or hold him, or in fact any of the children, and I knew it upset her a great deal. I now carried Paul around in a baby chair, in and out of the car. It was easier! I had always played down how much behind he was to his grandparents. I didn't want to hurt them. I assumed that Susan wuld be all right to cope with him, especially as Joe and Annette knew my routine. After all, she had been a nurse, coping with all sorts of situations before she married Mark's dad.

However, when we arrived back I knew that things had gone wrong. Mark's mum was sitting out in the kitchen and I went in to see her whilst Mark took the presents upstairs.

"Hello, Mum, I hope the kids haven't been too exhausting

for you!"

I saw the kitchen in general disarray and a pile of dirty dishes stacked in the sink. Her face was pale, and her eyes tearful.

"Carrie! Don't you realise just how badly retarded Paul is? He can't even chew properly and swallow minced meat!" She was crying by now, her head in her hands. "How could my son have a child like that?"

I felt angry. How dare she!

"A child like that, as you put it, is my son as well, and slow or not I love him, and I'm proud of him! So he needs a bit of extra help. I'm here to give it."

I tried to sound convincing, without letting her be aware that the misery was busy circulating inside me. Judging by her reply I had achieved this.

"You are a hard woman, Carrie, just to accept it like that. You don't know what it will do to Mark!"

But I did. I also knew in spite of my optimistic words, what it was doing to me. I realised now that it had been the wrong thing to do to ask her to look after Paul. Not only was it very hard work, I had also succeeded in upsetting her, too. I knew now I could never ask her again!

Chapter Nine

I knew that Paul and I were gradually becoming isolated from the outside world, but the only way that I could cope with the criticism of him was to protect him by removing him from the situation. I started to become a bit of a recluse and only left the house when it was absolutely necessary. I was fiercely trying to guard him from the cruelties of the outside world, when really I should have helped him to face up to it, and myself also. It was a coward's way out, and when I see it in retrospect I know what I did only made the situation worse, particularly for me. Paul would smile at me in recognition now, and in response if his name was spoken, but if anyone strange came into the room he kept his head lowered and avoided all eye contact with them. I was happier when Joe and Annette were around. Their constant contact with him, kissing, hugging him, and showing him their toys, seemed to rouse him for brief intervals from his egocentric little world. He would smile at them, too, and his dad, and Joe was so thrilled when he put one of his Matchbox cars into Paul's hand one day, and he turned it over and examined it, whilst laughing with delight. The next time that Joe got his pocket money he went out to buy Paul a car and was delighted to see his response. Over the years he helped him to build quite a collection of cars and taught him how to hold them and push them along the floor.

Mark had thrown himself into work, doing all the overtime he could, and I rarely saw him. I found it difficult to face him when I did, and one day, in a fit of extreme depression, I took the children and went.

I was borrowing the flat belonging to a friend who had

gone abroad for a year. I knew this was only a temporary breathing space and it gave me time to try and sort out my life. Mark accepted it after a while, providing that I allowed the children to go and stay with him every other weekend. I had found it hard to take his children away from him, so I readily agreed. He gave me a sum of money in settlement and I signed away my right to own half of our house. I was on my own now, but by my own volition! I bought a small haberdashery business and rented the maisonette above it, and it gave me a chance to earn enough for us to survive and still keep Paul by my side.

My new doctor suggested that Paul should have half an hour of physiotherapy at the hospital every day to try and stimulate his limbs into action. I had repeatedly tried to sit him up, but he always went rigid and threw himself back, yelling loudly as though in pain. I did not want to risk hurting him, so after a while I gave up.

I managed to arrange the physiotherapy at lunch-time, whilst the shop was closed, and each day found me closing the door at one o'clock and driving Paul to our local hospital. The sessions were not a success. The nurses persevered every day for a month, trying to stimulate his limbs, massaging and trying to help him to use them. Paul had angry rages! He objected to the contact and strongly fought against co-operating in any way. He spent the whole of the time he was there howling with extreme indignation. On the final occasion his anger induced an asthma attack, his first really bad one. I was really frightened. His lips turned blue, and his face was grey! He had coughed himself into such a state of agitation that he was fighting for breath. He had to be rushed to the children's ward and was put inside an oxygen tent. He spent three more days in hospital recovering from it. After he was allowed to come home I returned to the doctor. He had now received a report from the hospital, and knew that the attempts at physiotherapy had proved futile. He asked me if I would object to Paul going to Great Ormond Street, the famous childrens' hospital in London, to see if they could find out any more about Paul's problems. I agreed readily because I knew whatever the problem we needed to face up to it and deal with it in the best way possible. Somehow, ever since I had been told by Dr Pearson that Paul would not live beyond five years, when she had wrongly diagnosed his problem, nothing that had happened since had ever seemed so bad, because he would go on living. I suppose in a way she had done me a favour. It had made me realise in moments when I indulged in self-pity, that things could be a lot worse!

So, at the age of twenty months Paul went into Great Ormond Street for a ten day stay, and was given every test possible to find the answer to his retardation. I was able to be up there with him because of my new friend, Annie. My friendship with her had come about because of the children. Annette was now at the local primary school and she had a friend, Lynne, who was a shy, quiet little girl. They were like chalk and cheese. This friendship was to last for many years and continue into adult life. Lynne's mother, Annie, was an extrovert, just what I needed in my life at that time! She was very down-to-earth and honest, and the thing that warmed me to her most of all was her acceptance of Paul as he was and her readiness to help out with him if needed. I must admit, apart from Mark, who had always been very good with his children, I was now in the habit of seeing to all Paul's needs myself. Joe and Annette, at their tender years, had only just mastered the art of nappy changing. Annie offered to run the shop for me and this left me free to visit Paul every day. Mark was also going to come up as often as he could.

The first day when I took Paul up there I felt low, and I entered the ward where he was to be staying with great misgivings. Hospitals were places that I did not feel comfortable in and I was feeling rather bitter. Why should this have happened to me? Why my son? Why anyone's really?

The nurse was brisk and efficient, but caring too.

"Hello, Paul! Hello, mum! This is his cot. Please put him in there. We need to take some more details and he will be having tests later. Would he like a drink do you think?"

"Yes, he does get thirsty, but he prefers fruit juice. Milky drinks make his eczema worse and he cannot eat eggs. He is allergic to them."

"Right! I'll make a note of all this." She scribbled on a

47

pad. "Is he allergic to any medicines?"

"I'm not sure. He only has Ventolin and Nuelin syrup for his wheezing."

"Right, and I know you've been asked all these questions before, but we need to go through it all again."

I was used to it by now. Details of my pregnancy, my labour, his birth. Then his development. When did his asthma and eczema start?

"Does any of this give you any clues?"

"You never know! We have to have a picture to work on, and obviously the more you can tell us the more it helps."

I had placed Paul in the cot my now. He lay looking up at the bars, a faraway look in his deep blue eyes. His eyes flickered over and met mine briefly, and held them just for a moment. He chuckled with delight, but when the nurse spoke to him he frowned and turned his head away. It was only momentary and when he saw the lights, which were on because it was a dull day, he appeared to be fascinated and he stared at them.

"He is very shy." I said defensively. "He has to get to know you before he smiles."

"Don't worry. I understand. He certainly knows his mum!"

I felt a wave of protective pride inside me. I suppose anyone who has a baby that starts to smile and respond at the normal age would be amazed that at twenty months this could mean so much to me. The truth was, that unlike other babies, Paul reserved his smiles and displays of happiness for his family and the people who took the trouble to get to know him. Therefore it was special to us because he treated us as if we were special in his life.

"If you want you can go down to the canteen now and get some lunch. If you come back after three o'clock Paul will be back from his tests."

That seemed a good idea. I remembered that I hadn't eaten. This morning I had felt too churned up about bringing him to the hospital, but I was now feeling a bit more able to cope.

Mark had planned to come and spend some time with him from late afternoon to evening, because he knew that I would want to get back to Joe and Annette. I liked to be there after

48

school for them. They were very good about it, but they mattered to me too.

I went down the corridor and found the canteen. Although it was warm in the hospital the weather was cold, so I had a bowl of steaming hot oxtail soup with a crusty roll. After I had eaten this I sat for a while trying to relax. This was always something I found hard to do. After a while I looked at my watch. It was still only two o'clock. Another hour to go yet! I went for a walk and when I left the hospital grounds I had a look around the local shops which were nearby. Eventually the time passed and I made my way back up to the ward to see Paul. His cot was empty but the nurse smiled and told me to wait because he would be back at any minute.

As I was sitting nervously awaiting his return I noticed a mother with her little boy, probably aged three years, in the next bay. The curtains were not drawn and as I glanced over I saw the surgeon go in there. He had obviously performed some sort of operation to correct a physical problem on the child, and I could not help hearing the mother say, excitedly, "He can walk now, Mr Ross! You must see him walk!"

"Of course, I've been waiting all day for this!" he said, smiling. She tentatively let go of the little boy's hands. He stood gingerly balanced, and we all held our breath. Then he slowly took a few steps, staggering into the waiting arms of the surgeon. I will never forget the looks of proud delight on all their faces. The mother scooped her little boy into her arms, saying, "I can never thank you enough Mr Ross. It's only thanks to you he can walk."

Well, I thought, if Mr Ross can help them maybe he can help Paul!

c

Chapter Ten

I was not given any information about Paul's results until they were complete. So I waited anxiously, worrying and wondering constantly. I saw other children with their problems too, and it was disturbing to see how these other little mites suffered. On the second day Paul was put into a ward with other children and I noticed there was another cot in the next bay. There did not appear to be anyone visiting and I could hear the sound of a baby gently cooing, so I peeped in to say hello. There was a dear little boy laying there, but his arms and legs were all twisted up around him as if his limbs were broken. I jumped back in alarm. Surely he must be in pain! He caught my eye and gave me the most radiant smile. The nurse appeared.

"I see you've found Tommy. It's nice for someone to talk to him. His parents live in Wales and cannot visit very often."

I burst out quickly, "I saw his poor little arms and legs! What a tragedy. He smiled at me, and yet I would have thought that he hadn't got much to smile about."

She shrugged and looked sad, briefly, "He's not in pain, but I agree, he hasn't much in life to look forward to."

I gave him one last look, stroking his little forehead. He had such a merry smile. I felt a choking feeling of pity for the little mite and had to walk away from his cot.

This memory stayed with me. Later the same day, in an effort to occupy my mind in a useful way, I took Paul and made my way to the playroom to see if I could interest him in some toys to play with. He was a bit fed up because he had had blood tests and samples of urine taken from him during the day. The urine sample was collected after

50

an hour of nurses having to check his nappy every ten minutes, and Paul very much resented the interference. He had also been 'wired up', as I jokingly called it. I was allowed to attend this test to try and keep him happy. The procedure was to put what looked like electric plugs all around his head. It took twenty minutes to set them up, if he didn't pull them out! It was to test for brain damage. I had done my best, talking to him and showing him cars, and eventually the test had been completed.

So now we were on our way to the day room, and I carried Paul in my arms, wishing I had brought his buggy. He was heavy! A lady fell into step beside me, smiling at Paul, and asked me if he was enjoying his stay. I grimaced and explained it was for tests which he didn't like, but nevertheless had to be done. She agreed, "Yes, I think they're very good here. They've been marvellous to John, my son."

I wasn't sure what was wrong with him, so I didn't quite know what to say. I knew that some of the children were seriously ill, some with leukaemia and dying, but this lady seemed so cheerful. I didn't have to wait long to find out. She told me, "He's ten years old, and his brain cells are dying. . . . Six months ago he was playing football with his friends and now he is in a wheel-chair. I know that soon he won't even recognise me."

I looked at her in horror. What could I say? I felt any words would be inadequate. Should I offer sympathy? She had said it all in a flat emotionless voice, as though it was an everyday thing. But I knew only too well how shock and grief can affect you, and I was very moved. I pressed her hand.

"I can see God is giving you the strength to cope."

We had reached the door of the day room now, and I saw the thin little figure in the wheel-chair with the emaciated face, but the determination to go on living a bit longer was apparent. He couldn't speak or even move his arms, but the recognition in his eyes was obvious. He struggled to put some life into his wasted muscles, and with a supreme effort made a nodding gesture in his mother's direction, whilst uttering an animal-like noise from his throat. His mother showed her delight in seeing him and strode purposefully over to his wheel-chair. She kissed the sunken cheek. "I know you hate your mum kissing you. You think you're too old, but I love you." I heard the catch in her throat. Then she firmly grasped the handle of the wheel-chair and took him for a walk, manoeuvring it out of the day room, and waving to Paul on the way out.

I just sat there for a few minutes cuddling Paul whilst he turned a car over in his hand, examining it from all angles. He was beginning to allow me contact without getting angry, and I found it soothing after seeing those two little boys with terrible problems that could never be rectified. Those memories have never left me and in times of depression, which I have had over the years, I have always reminded myself that there is always someone else worse off if you look around you. I try to count my blessings these days and be grateful for everything that I've got. I shall never forget the courage of that woman who knew her son was dying, and I hope she found comfort in God to help her through her grief afterwards.

After a while I looked at the time and regretfully realised that I would have to go. Mark was due to arrive soon, and I knew he would play with Paul and help to give him his tea. I was wishing that this stay in hospital would pass quickly so that our life could go back to normal.

Annie was being marvellous. Coping with the shop she found to be no great problem as February was a very quiet month for shopping, so I tried to be back for when the children arrived home from school. Luckily we lived near to the local primary school and Joe was enjoying being thought of as grown up bringing both Annette and Lynne home with him. It's amazing how families, even with young children, can rally together in time of need!

Mark arrived and picked up Paul, hugging him with delight. I felt a pang of guilt for all that had gone wrong between us.

"How did his tests go?"

"They haven't told me yet. We will know at the end of the week, but all the pulling him about upset him a little."

As I spoke I looked towards Paul. He was seated on top of Mark's shoulders, pulling at his hair and shrieking with delight. I was relieved to see him so happy, and I felt happier

52

at leaving him. Mark reminded me, "I shall pop round to see Joe and Annette later in the week after I come from here. What time do they go to bed?"

"About eight o'clock usually, but if I know you're coming I'll keep them up."

"OK, I'll ring you to confirm when."

I smiled my thanks awkwardly, and slipped off after kissing Paul who was still enjoying sitting up high on his dad's shoulders.

Each day at the hospital followed in a similar routine, and the day that Paul was due to leave hospital we were visited by Mr Ross, the surgeon, for the analysis of the final results. Mark and I were seated on chairs, on either side of Paul's cot waiting, and he entered the ward and stood facing us.

"Well, Mr and Mrs Benson, I have done every test that I know to get to the root of the problem, but I haven't got any definite answers."

I was staring at him, thinking, another anticlimax!

"He takes more notice of us than he did a few months ago," said Mark desperately.

"Yes, you must encourage every little bit of development." He smiled at us kindly and continued talking.

"Paul does not fall into any sort of category. He is not a mongol. He shows signs of autism, but the hardest thing of all is that he battles against wanting to develop. You could almost say that he is self-destructive!"

He had not finished yet, only pausing to ascertain our reaction.

"That is another problem facing a handicapped child. They lack the desire to learn and need constant stimulation. I have checked his back and there is no physical reason to stop him from learning to sit up and maybe even walk one day, but his attitude of mind is such that he cannot be bothered."

"I see." My mind was racing. "But what has caused these problems? Did I do anything wrong during my pregnancy?"

"I'm sure you didn't, Mrs Benson. However, one thing we did notice which had been overlooked on your file before," he paused and I listened intently. "You had a blood test done early in your pregnancy and then another done at eight months. The later test detected antibodies present that were synonymous with someone who had suffered German Measles. If this occurred early in the pregnancy it has a harmful effect on the foetus."

"But doctor," I was incredulous, "I felt so well all the way through!"

He cleared his throat. "We can never be sure whether there was a fault with the foetus right from conception, or whether it occurred later, but it is something that has happened and the only thing we do know for sure is that he will need help for all of his life."

My thoughts were busy. So we would never really know the cause. We would go on blaming ourselves for ever. Was it better or worse to not know where the fault lay? On that day I vowed that Paul would sit up and walk. No matter how long it took I would teach him! He did not have a sentence of death hanging over him and I was going to make the quality of his life as good as it was possible to!

Chapter Eleven

Now that I knew that I was not hurting Paul's back by propping him up I got to work on him. At first he reacted in exactly the same way as he had at physiotherapy. He went rigid with anger, but I knew that I had to show him that sitting up was fun! I laid him on my lap and massaged his back. He stopped howling after a while because he found it soothing. Then I tried sitting him up and massaging his back at the same time. We had good days and bad days! If he was wheezy he would regress back within himself and I would have to forget working with him for that day. It was a good lesson for me to learn to cultivate patience. After about a month the protests stopped and he became passive. This was followed by a small degree of co-operation, which was very heartening. Maybe he had become tired of viewing the world from floor level, or else just sitting in a baby chair. I worked on him twice a day now, and little by little I watched him raise his head and try to sit up. This gave me a wonderful fillip, and on his second birthday, whilst he was propped against the settee on the floor, something caused Joe to rush out into the kitchen full of excitement. "Mum! Mum! Come and see Paul! He sat up alone without leaning against the settee!"

I rushed in and there was Paul, holding his back straight and laughing, whilst Annette dangled his favourite car in front of him. We were all so thrilled that we hugged each other and cried with happiness. This meant so much to us!

Not long after that he discovered he could get around by shuffling on his bottom, and this became his means of transport from then onwards. This added to our happiness.

My life was still pretty well wrapped around him. I never left him with other people because I wasn't sure whether they would understand his needs. Having the shop was perfect, because it allowed me to keep him near me whilst I was working. It was hard work for me bringing up the children alone, but it had been my choice to leave Mark, so I had no reason to be bitter. I never denied him access to them because he loved them dearly, and they went to stay with him every other weekend. Sometimes Paul didn't go because it was harder for Mark to cope with him on his own, and if he wanted to take them swimming, or to stay out later in the evening, you could never be sure that Paul would not get wheezy. Changes in routine set him off, and this spoilt the outing for everyone. So he spent most of his time with me. Annie offered to look after him if I ever wanted to go out, but I always felt anxious when parted from him. Also, having worked all day in the shop, after I had put the children to bed I was really tired. Annie often came round in the evening with Lynne. She was now divorced and so was lonely too. I found her extrovert personality very amusing. She had an amazing sense of humour, seeing the funny side of everything, and above all else she always treated Paul normally. He always had a smile for her and as he reserved his smiles only for the special people in his life I knew that he liked her.

Joe and Annette were very mature for children of their tender years. As a family we were close. They dearly loved Paul and accepted his handicaps without question. Over the years they were to suffer much ridicule and taunting from other children who came to our house and saw Paul, but they learnt to handle it with dignity. Many of their friends were won over by their attitude to accept Paul as he was and they were the friends who remained constant over the years. It's amazing how something like that can sort out the genuine people from the others.

I was learning not to be so sensitive and hurt by careless remarks. I had to develop a harder exterior to survive emotionally. I had not told my parents too much about Paul's handicap, and led them to believe that he would improve as he grew up. Indeed I believed that myself!

56

It kept me going. My mother was very sensitive about Paul. She had lost two babies, one boy soon after birth, and a girl at two years old during an asthma attack. Her health was suffering now, too. Her arms and legs were stiff with rheumatoid arthritis, and although she loved all her grandchildren she had difficulty now even in cuddling them on her lap. She told me how useless she felt at being unable to help with Paul or look after him when I went out. I told her cheerfully not to worry. "He's OK, Mum! When he's ready, he'll run around like the others."

So you could say that my life revolved around the children, and I couldn't see it changing much for many years yet. Joe and Annette were both learning to swim, and Joe had also joined the Cubs. Now that I had my own car I managed to find time to take them after the shop was closed. During the school holidays I took the children out once a week on Wednesdays, when my shop was shut. For a treat I took them out for lunch. They sat at the table, helping to wipe Paul's sticky fingers, and people frequently commented about my bonny children. Paul's table manners were good, and he fed himself well now. Sitting in a high chair he was just like any other young child, and I wanted to get him used to eating in public and behaving normally.

On Sundays we visited my parents, but it saddened me to see my mother slowing up. In spite of all our beseeching she would not go to the doctor for a long time, but when the pain became unbearable she finally went in desperation. He gave her some pain killers but told her that unless she was prepared to go into hospital and have her hands put in wax, which was a new treatment, there was nothing else he could do for her. Mum, of course, declined. She would not leave my dad and my brother, who still lived at home, to fend for themselves, and I also think she was frightened that she wouldn't come out again. I was also dreading the day when she would end up in a wheel-chair, as already she could no longer walk very far.

When Mark and I had been parted for a year but were still not divorced, Jeff came into my life. I already knew him as a friend of Mark's from work, and I had also heard that his marriage had broken up before we parted, and that he had gone back to live with his mother.

One Wednesday, when I was in Croydon with the children, I met him in the High Street. We were doing some Christmas shopping and the children were very excited. He stopped to talk to me. Paul was in the buggy and Annette in her usual effervescent way was bouncing all round the pavement.

"Mummy! I thought we were seeing Father Christmas!"

"Annette, wait! Mummy is talking!" from Joe.

I turned to reassure her that I hadn't forgotten, but Jeff was first.

"Don't let me hold you up. It was nice to see you, Carrie."

"Bye, Jeff, if you're passing the shop on any day except Wednesday come in for a coffee."

He smiled. "I will!"

We moved on and went into the department store, making our way to the grotto in the basement. I had to park the buggy and carry Paul in my arms.

When they went in it had to be Annette first. She was always the more daring one. After a few minutes she came out, happily clutching a Barbie doll and a set of fashion clothes for it. "Go on, Joe," she urged. "Just tell him what you want for Christmas. He can bring it," she added with great conviction.

Joe was more sceptical. "Don't be silly! He doesn't know where we live."

"He does, I told him!"

Annette would always have the last word, but she still believed in Father Christmas. Joe was eight years old and beginning to get his doubts about it. He approached the entrance to the grotto, tentatively. Curiosity got the better of him and he went in. Whilst we were waiting, Annette was thinking, and she remarked, "Paul should see Father Christmas!"

I clutched him to me, but he was happy looking at the Christmas tree and all the coloured decorations. He loved bright lights. I said quickly, "But he might cry! You know what he can be like with strangers."

Her face dropped with disappointment, and I felt mean.

Joe emerged carrying a large Tonka lorry, which pleased him because he collected them. Father Christmas walked

58

out behind him.

"What about the little boy? What toys does he like?"

"Oh! But I haven't paid for him."

Annette brightened up. "He loves Matchbox cars."

Father Christmas stretched out his arms to Paul and to my amazement Paul stroked his red coat, then he touched his white beard. He went to him unprotestingly, sitting on his lap and staring at him with wide-eyed innocence. Then the moment passed and his attention strayed back to the big tree. Father Christmas found him a parcel in his sack, and together we helped Paul unwrap it. Inside there was a pack of four Matchbox cars, which pleased him. Joe and Annette were delighted.

"Look Mum! More for his collection!"

I thanked Father Christmas, feeling a little embarrassed. He refused to take any extra money from me and as he handed Paul back to me he gave me a broad wink.

I came out of the store feeling happy and pleased that Paul had something too. I had promised to take the children to McDonald's for lunch, and when we collected our order and sat down, there sitting at the next table was Jeff.

Chapter Twelve

Jeff became a regular visitor in the evenings. I found it easy to confide in him about Paul. My worries and fears seemed less when shared! He was completely detached from the situation, no emotional ties like Mark. He listened intently and then said, "You spend too much of your life with Paul."

As I moved to protest, "Don't get me wrong, I admire your dedication, but have you ever thought about how he will cope when he goes to school. He is so dependent on you."

I considered his words. "I must admit I haven't! I can't put him in a nursery school because he can't walk and he's nearly three, but I suppose that one day he will go to school."

"Well, let's see if we can help him to walk."

This was easier said than done, as I well knew. Paul had perfected the art of shuffling around on his bottom, and he could reach anything he wanted. Therefore he had no desire to walk. Although his legs were thin and his muscles under-developed, the doctor had said that there was no reason to suspect he was spastic. However, on Jeff's advice I set to work again massaging his legs, and then persuaded Annie (she didn't need much persuading!) to run the shop for a couple of hours on a Saturday afternoon every other weekend, and we took him swimming.

By now Joe and Annette were both swimming well and had earnt numerous badges for distance. Annette had progressed well enough to be accepted by the local swimming club. They came along too and had fun playing in the water, and we worked on Paul. He loved the water and kicked his legs freely, and after a while his muscles started to develop.

Ever since he had been to hospital for physiotherapy and his anger had induced an asthma attack they had decided to abandon all efforts, just in case of a repeat performance. Now it was down to us.

Paul seemed to lack the confidence needed to try and stand up, except, of course, in water when he didn't quite realise he was doing it.

Jeff had two daughters from his marriage, of similar age to Joe and Annette, and they usually came over on Saturdays and joined us all to go swimming. Jeff also suggested that I should go out with him on a Friday evening once a fortnight and have a break from Paul. At first I protested but I knew he was right. I plucked up the courage, when the children were due at their dad's one weekend and asked Mark if he could have Paul on a regular basis to give me a break. He agreed, but when I told him it was because I wanted to go out with Jeff it went down like a leaded balloon.

"How can I do much for Joe and Annette? I was going to take them down the club!"

It was his local diving club. "They're having a bit of a party in the evening."

I hesitated guiltily, but remembered what Jeff had said. "Take them! I will see that Paul has a sleep in the afternoon and then he will last longer."

He reluctantly agreed, but I knew the main problem was Jeff. Mark had always hoped when I found the going tough we would get back together. He had the full backing and support of my parents who had told me that they thought I was crazy to leave him. They were not keen on my friendship with Jeff, and had told me quite bluntly that his intentions could not be good because, "You are not exactly a marriage prospect with three children plus the problems you will have in bringing Paul up."

I knew this was true. I didn't think that I was a good marriage prospect either. My confidence was not at its highest because of what had happened to me. A person who has not had the experience of having a handicapped child would have no idea of what it does to you. It made me feel inadequate as a person. At times I could not help looking at other babies, and young children and their mothers, and wondering why it had happened to me? Why to anyone?

Then my conscience would bother me. How ungrateful I was! I had three lovely children, Paul included, because I knew that I loved him dearly, but I wanted the best for him in life and I felt he had been born with so many problems he didn't deserve. So my emotions were in turmoil and sometimes I could feel really depressed. I tried hard not to feel bitter. I had to carry on normally for the sake of my children, but often at night I would weep, in the privacy of my bedroom, for my darling little boy and all the problems he had been born with.

I didn't really know if I wanted a man in my life. I had already failed one, I felt. The children were the centre of my life and there was nothing but pressure from everyone around me about my friendship with Jeff. But he was a good listener. It helped to talk to him and he confided his problems to me, too. The thing that amazed me was that he wasn't put off being with me by the children. I had very little time to spare for him and he frequently saw me when I was feeling low.

Nevertheless, not long after our divorces both became final he asked me to marry him, and although I was full of reservations as to whether it would work or not, it did not stop me from accepting.

Chapter Thirteen

For the first year I wondered many times if I had made a mistake in marrying Jeff, and I'm sure he must have felt the same way about me, too! Initially Joe and Annette were difficult and when he asked them to do things they played up, but after a while they came round. I think they realised that it was nice to have a man around the house again, and so did I. Jeff was always willing to take them swimming which they enjoyed so much. One day Annette came to me and said, "If Uncle Jeff doesn't mind Joe and I want to call him Dad, even though he's not our real dad. Our real one will always be Daddy," she added loyally. This made me feel very happy. Now we could be a proper family.

But unfortunately it wasn't to be roses all the way for us. Jeff was not impressed by the fact that I had to get up every night and go to Paul when he woke up coughing. I slept lightly and would stumble out of bed, half asleep, and go to settle him before he got too wheezy. After Jeff had suffered a week of this, one night he took over as I went to get out of bed when the now all too familiar coughing started. He said impatiently, "Don't rush into him. He's trying to get your attention!"

"But he might have an asthma attack if I don't."

But Jeff persisted with his theory. "Just see how he goes. Have you ever thought that because he can't talk it's a way of attracting your attention."

I held back, reluctantly, anxious for what might happen. It was OK for Jeff. He wasn't emotionally involved, I thought. How would he feel if it was his son! I waited, uncertain, and after about five minutes he started wailing and I could hear the sound of wheezing.

"Now look what's happened!" I shouted accusingly, and rushed into Paul's room. I felt panicky, watching his laboured breathing. I stroked his forehead, wondering whether I should call the doctor. Sometimes I did this and by the time that he arrived it had passed and Paul was all right.

I heard Jeff's step behind me and I still felt angry with him for encouraging me to ignore Paul's coughing, but he was undaunted.

"Well, young man, you might fool your mother, but you don't fool me! There's nothing wrong with you. I want to see you drink your orange juice and then lie down and go to sleep without this silly wheezing."

I turned to him in amazement.

"He can't help it, Jeff! and he doesn't understand you." I was still cross at his apparent lack of consideration.

"Yes, he can help it. He plays on your soft nature and he *does* understand what we say. He *is* handicapped, but he's *not* stupid!"

I had to admit that Jeff was right. He had, with his firm determined voice, penetrated Paul's closed in little world, and although Paul was now scowling because he didn't like being told off, a thing that rarely happened normally, it worked. He drank his orange noisily, and his breathing seemed to settle down almost immediately. He pulled the sheet up over his face and closed his eyes. We went back to bed, and although it didn't always work, because sometimes his wheezing was genuine, in the years to come, if he heard Jeff call out for him to stop, he obeyed.

Jeff gradually took control of the children. When I look back now I suppose they needed it. They had spent over a year on their own with me, without any male influence, and I had probably spoilt them a little. But as a family we were very close. We shared our problems together, and there was a great deal of loyalty. I spent some of the time being grateful for his strength and firmness when I needed support and the other half resenting his intrusion. He was a man who liked to dominate, and this caused many arguments because I like to be myself and make my own decisions. We had lots of disputes about the children. We didn't agree about the way to bring them up. Jeff believed in strict discipline and I thought they were too young for such firm measures. But after a while things settled down and we became a happier family. There was still a feeling of animosity from both our ex-married partners, not unsurprisingly, but we coped with it. Luckily, since Jeff had married me, my parents had changed their attitude towards him, which made me feel a lot happier.

I woke up one morning feeling very sick, and in fact I was. The day before I had eaten fish, unlike everyone else. They all had eaten spaghetti bolognese, so I thought maybe the fish had been a little off. I felt nauseous all day and so after Jeff had arrived home from work I went to the doctor.

I went in and sat down, and he greeted me. "Hello, it's Mrs Carter now, I see. How are you?"

I told him my symptoms. He was writing, and looked up, "Last period, when?"

I suddenly realised it had been a while. "My life is so busy, doctor. I hadn't realised!" It suddenly struck me. Pregnant again! I wasn't sure how I felt. Could I cope with another child? How would Jeff feel?

I was surprised because he had told me that because of an illness he'd had that he was unlikely to father any more children.

The doctor asked, "How old is little Paul now?"

"Just three, doctor."

"We need to get him to school! You must have breathing space now. There's a very good special school about five miles away. He would be picked up and dropped from the coach every day. How do you feel about it?"

How did I feel? Anxious . . . apprehensive . . . relieved . . . ! A mixture of feelings as usual. I gulped and drew my breath. I hadn't realised that sending him to school would hurt. I had wrapped him up in a protective cocoon.

"As long as he doesn't pine for me, doctor."

"He won't. Most of the time Paul is in his own little world, you know," he said gently. "You as his mother can penetrate it occasionally, but you must realise that most of the time he is wrapped up in himself."

I did, and that's why the occasional responses we were able to elicit from him were so precious to us.

"Yes, doctor. As long as they know how to cope if he gets wheezy."

"They will. But now back to you, my dear. You must rest assured that you will have every possible care taken of you during your pregnancy. However . . . " he stopped, searching for the right words to say, "you are, unfortunately, after your previous pregnancy, known as a High Risk Mother!"

I stared at him comprehending all he said with horror! He went on.

"I can offer you the needle test of the amniotic fluid to ascertain whether the baby is normal or not. If it is not, then the choice is yours. No one would expect you to bring up two handicapped children!"

The full realisation of what he was saying struck me. I could go through the same nightmare again! He was offering me a legal abortion if necessary. But I knew I couldn't do it to Jeff. It was our child. I might end up letting him down, letting everyone down, but I had to take the risk, and pray to God it wouldn't happen again. I heard myself say, "Thank you, doctor. I would rather not know. I will love my baby, no matter what!"

He never mentioned it again, and I went home to break the news.

Jeff, Joe and Annette were delighted that I was pregnant. I was thrilled too that Jeff and I would have our own child. He was good to mine, and I felt we deserved to share one of our own.

The pregnancy was not a good one. I was obviously apprehensive and I was plagued by sickness all the way through. I couldn't keep much food down, and although the doctor checked me regularly, and couldn't find any reason for it, I was mostly existing on lucozade and tonic water.

During this time another mile-stone was reached with Paul. He discovered that he could stand up. He could not be coaxed to move, but he would stand, leaning against a chair, chuckling with delight to himself at this new accomplishment. Also, to my great surprise, he became clean and dry during the day. I had always managed to catch him after meals on the potty, ever since he had learnt to sit up. Now it seemed his body had been trained like a robot to go only at these times. We were all very proud of him and praised him highly, but I took the precaution of keeping nappies on him at night.

He had coped very well with school. His teachers had fallen in love with his cheeky face and big blue eyes. It was also more noticeable how he put his head up when he was praised, looked you straight in the face and showed you how happy he was. Praise meant a lot to Paul.

So, my pregnancy passed, and then after a long and complicated labour, very similar to the one I'd had with Annette, and one month early, Amy was born.

Chapter Fourteen

Amy was a healthy baby, small in weight, six pounds five ounces, but the doctors assured me, quite an adequate weight for an eight month baby. She was a little jaundiced, but that passed off after a few days.

Jeff had been with me when she was born and although I knew that he had hoped for a boy, I felt relieved that she was a girl. My instincts told me she was normal, and I never really worried about her development. She had the same fair colouring as the others, but facially she was a feminine version of Jeff to a tee. I breast-fed her too, and after a few days the hospital allowed me to take her home.

Joe and Annette were so thrilled when they saw her, but Paul took no interest. She was just like a doll to him. Jeff was very proud of her, and I think was particularly chuffed at this miniature caricature of himself.

So we settled back into our family routine, and the first year of Amy's life sped by. She learnt everything very quickly. She was always a bright and enquiring child, and somehow it seemed to rub off a little on Paul. At eight months she started walking along the furniture and I came in one day to find him following after her. What a happy day that was for us! Joe and Annette were now ten and eight and were exceptionally well domesticated for children of their age. I would sometimes wake up on a Sunday morning to find Joe with a tray of tea to greet Jeff and I. Annette would then come in and inform us, "Both the babies' bottoms have been changed, and they've had a drink of fruit juice."

I was so proud of them and I think, looking back, I realise that kids often become more independent when their mother is not available to do everything for them. If they were jealous of the little ones they certainly never showed it. By now Annette had become quite a proficient swimmer for the local club. She trained three nights a week, and was swimming in the club galas. She also belonged to the Brownies, and Joe was a Cub.

When Amy was a year old she took her first steps. Not to be outdone, within a week, Paul also took his first staggering steps and I was there to catch him. He has never progressed much beyond the unsteady gait of a toddler to this day, but nevertheless it was wonderful to us, and more than we could have ever dared to hope for in the past. We often wondered if, without Amy to copy, Paul would have had the confidence to do it, and take the plunge on his own. As Paul was now five years old, and able to walk a little way, life seemed a lot brighter. If we went shopping or for long walks he sat in the double buggy with Amy, but he was able to toddle around at home. He was still not greatly interested in toys, other than his cars, but at school he was being taught to thread beads and do simple jigsaw puzzles. You had to sit down with him, which I didn't have much time for, but Joe and Annette did. Now he was developing his personality, and if he was in an unco-operative mood the whole jigsaw would be flung in the air, and he had developed the habit of biting his knuckle with frustration when things were not going how he wanted. I found this very distressing, as he was making his hand so sore. On one of his check ups the doctor told me I would have to expect this as the frustration when things were going wrong for him was caused because he couldn't talk.

"You don't realise that as he gets older, Paul is falling more into the category of an autistic child, do you?" enquired the doctor.

"Autism?" I had heard of this. Messages to the brain became confused.

"Yes, some autistic children learn to talk, some never do, but it causes frustration and, I'm afraid, violent moods when they can harm themselves and other people."

"My little Paul, harm others, never! For a start he's so small for his age. He's more the size of a three-year-old."

"Well, he will grow, Mrs Carter. I am just trying to prepare you in case it ever happens."

Paul was sitting demurely on my lap. He was ignoring our conversation, his big blue eyes staring ahead through the window. He had grown into a very bonny boy. His white blond hair was wavy, and his eyes had retained their startlingly blue colour. Matched with his fair skin, from which the naevus on his face had virtually disappeared, it gave him a most angelic appearance. The thought of him harming others was totally foreign to me, and I dismissed it from my mind. I went home from the doctor's with him and hoped his feelings of frustration would not manifest themselves too often for his sake.

As time passed and Amy started to talk we began to wonder if Paul would try and copy her sounds. It was clear that he understood most of what we said to him. He could obey commands, and often, if I asked someone else to do something, like to go upstairs and get my shoes, or bag, or similar, if they weren't quick, Paul would beat them to it. This was a game he loved playing. If he wanted something he would hold my arm, and then guide me towards it, and he nodded his head to express yes and no. I always found him easy to understand, but I knew that he sometimes flung himself on the floor and wept at school if he could not make them understand. This bothered me to think how frustrated he must feel and so attempts were made to teach him Makaton sign language. This was used by deaf people. He learnt a few signs in his own fashion, and I even went along for two evenings a week, for an hour after school, to learn how to use it to him. But Paul was clever enough to get through to all of us in his own way without sign language, and he could not be coaxed to use it at home.

As he had now turned five and was still presenting me with a dirty nappy every morning, I had despaired of ever getting him clean and dry at night. One morning, as I went into the room he shared with Joe, to be greeted by the familiar pungent odour, Jeff stood at the doorway, grimacing.

"He should get up and go to the toilet instead of giving you that rotten lot! Yes, young man!"

Paul lowered his gaze from Jeff's accusing stare, and I

intervened. "I can't risk the mess on the sheets, Jeff!"

"Just try him tonight. He knows where the toilet is, and he can walk."

It made sense. If I didn't try it he would never learn, but I did it with strong reservations. I woke him up at eleven o'clock, when we went to bed, and I guided his sleepy progress to the toilet. He obliged me by passing a small amount of urine.

When Jeff came up with my usual cup of tea in bed in the morning I heard Paul's familiar cough. I moved to get out of bed. Jeff stopped me gently.

"It's OK, he's on the loo."

"Oh! Did he have an accident?"

"No. I think we've caught him before he goes. Drink up your tea and then you can take over."

Jeff did not like dirty bottoms! He had not changed Amy's nappy very often and as she was now out of them he wasn't likely to have to now! When I entered the bathroom and found Paul had obliged us I was delighted. I gave him a kiss and lots of praise. He loved to be told that he was a clever boy! This became the routine. Jeff got him up early every morning, and somehow Paul instinctively knew that was when he should use the toilet. If we slept later he would wake up at that time and cough until he was told to go and sit on the toilet. Eventually, over a period of time, he learnt to get up and take himself when he needed to go, and never once did he have an accident! We were very proud of this achievement.

Life seemed a little less hard work for me, and now that Paul was going swimming and playing ball games, and generally exercising himself at school, he came home totally shattered at the end of the day. He was sleeping more soundly and I was getting out of bed to him less frequently at night. I could take him out to eat and to parties. He was eating very cleanly and handled a spoon and fork well. The doctor was very enthusiastic about his progress at his development check up.

"Well done to everyone! It's amazing how much a caring family environment can rub off. He's made much more progress than anyone could have expected."

"I have a very sensible husband who stands no nonsense,

71

and loyal children who help me with Paul a lot."

"Yes, it's a strong commitment which needs complete family unity. Do keep him at home for as long as you can."

I was shocked. Whatever did he mean? "I will keep him at home until I die, doctor. He's my son!" I spoke firmly.

Dr Roberts looked embarrassed. I must have sounded annoyed, but I couldn't believe that he would expect me not to keep Paul for ever within the family circle. So he needed help, but we were there to give him that.

I held his hand, trying to coax him to wave good-bye to the doctor, but he was not going to oblige me. The receptionist made us an appointment for six months time.

When we reached home Annie was there looking after Amy. She told me that my dad had telephoned to say that my mother was popping in to see us. My brother was bringing her up in his car. I hadn't seen her for about six weeks, so I was pleased, but I also felt a bit guilty, because we had been very busy lately and hadn't found the time to go and visit them. They lived about sixty miles away.

When she arrived I was startled to see that she had lost weight. However, she seemed her normal bright self and was as thrilled as ever to see her grandchildren. She loved them all, and battling against her difficulties to move her arms and legs, insisted that I lift her little ones on to her lap, one at a time, to be cuddled. Joe and Annette sat on either side of her whilst Amy, barefoot as usual, cuddled up to her, wiping fingers stained with coloured Smarties down her blouse. My mother was unconcerned at this, but I lifted Amy off to wipe her sticky fingers. I lifted Paul up and felt quite emotional when I saw the love in her eyes as she cuddled him, and he treated her to a solemn wide-eyed look from his big eyes. After Mum had gone I asked Jeff, "She doesn't look well. Do you think she worries about Paul? I always try to be optimistic about his progress."

"It's nothing that you do wrong. Don't blame yourself for everything. Maybe rheumatoid arthritis causes one to lose weight, but your mum's a fighter!"

I knew that this was true, but I still felt uneasy.

Two days later my dad telephoned to say that she was going into hospital for tests. He seemed cheerful, "She's a bit jaundiced but nothing to worry about."

We went to visit her in hospital, believing that she had only had a minor exploratory operation. She was very sleepy, and asked us to excuse her if she went to sleep. I kissed her good-bye and she sent her love to the children. I told her she would see them soon and that I would return later in the week to see her. She smiled, sleepily, and said, "Go now, darling! The children need you, especially little Paul."

The next morning my dad telephoned. His voice was hardly more than a whisper over the telephone. "Carrie, I'm afraid it's bad news. Your mother passed away last night!"

d

Chapter Fifteen

My mother's death affected me very deeply. It turned out that she had cancer, but that was not the reason for her death. She had suffered a post-operative complication known as peritonitis. I couldn't help thinking that maybe if the rheumatoid arthritis hadn't sapped her strength she would have survived! Who knows?

She was not old, only sixty-seven, and somehow I had always imagined she was immortal. Stupid really! Even though her health had declined and I knew she was already suffering I had imagined she would be around for a long time. She was a great loss in the lives of the children too, and this sudden amputation from her was cruel! I felt literally as though part of me was missing, and knew I would need time to adjust. Jeff was understanding, and the children were stoic.

We did not take them to the funeral. It wasn't fair. They were too young. When I saw the grief in the faces of my father and my brother I managed to control my own. It was worse for them. They had been living with her and had the sad task of disposing of her belongings. I went through the motions of talking to everyone politely, but my heart was with Mum, and I was wishing I could have her back again. There were so many things I hadn't said to her, such as how much I loved her and what a wonderful mother she'd always been to me. Don't we all when it's too late!

Mark had also been invited to the funeral, and we politely acknowledged one another. He understood why I had not brought the children. My mother had been very fond of him, and he of her too, I think. After everything was over and I kissed my dad and my brother, Rob, good-bye we returned home. I wondered how my dad would cope and wished that they lived a little nearer so that I could see them more often. They were coming up the following Sunday to spend the day with us, but sixty miles is a long way when you lead a busy life like I do. I vowed that I would remember to telephone them at least once a week to make sure that they were all right.

My solution to cope with the loss was to throw myself into work and keep busy. This was just as well, because our little haberdashery business was going well at the moment. This was encouraging, and I was kept busy. I had a regular group of customers that I tried hard to please and it seemed to be paying off.

The landlord had written to us, offering the freehold at a very cheap price because we were sitting tenants. As the accommodation above consisted of a three bedroomed maisonette and all the rooms were of generous size, we took the plunge and decided to buy. Finances were pretty tight with us. When Mark and I had split up I had agreed to accept a small lump sum, which I had used to purchase the business. The income from the shop paid the bills and fed us. Mark paid for the children's clothes and also holidays, but the rest was down to us. Although he had his own separate job as a telephone engineer, Jeff was heavily committed financially. He had to pay the mortgage on his ex-wife's home and also pay maintenance for his two daughters, so he didn't have much money left. Nevertheless, he worked out that we could have the mortgage paid by him if we took on a small part-time job to boost our incomes a little. The idea of owning our own home was very appealing, but to do this we had to work in the evenings too. He became the manager of a football charity, and we took it in turns to go out collecting rounds that had not been done, recruiting new people, and going to see collectors. Many of our friends thought that we were mad, but we were both of the opinion that if you want something badly enough then you can go out and get it for yourself. When I went collecting Joe and Annette came with me, and the rounds were done in a much quicker time, and they were happy because they were earning pocket money.

My mother, God bless her, had left me a small sum of money, and we used this to pay our deposit and also the legal fees for the purchase. Jeff felt much more enthusiastic about decorating now that we were buying, and he set to work to install central heating and redecorate. It was nice to have central heating upstairs with winter coming on, because Paul needed to be in a warm room to keep his breathing stable.

We didn't go out much socially. We couldn't really afford a baby-sitter as well as the cost of going out and there was the added worry that Paul might have an asthma attack. So we slipped into a way of life that really only involved work and more work. Jeff did work around the house in the evening if I was out collecting rounds, and at the weekend he did decorating. The house was looking nice and we had bought new carpets, but sometimes I thought it would be nice to go out and have a break. I loved the children but I needed a break from them at times.

Our daily routine continued in this way and after the summer of 1979 passed the trade in our shop seemed to die a death. This was an added worry, as our finances were not good and the shop rates were high. When I spoke to the other shopkeepers on our small parade it seemed to be the same for them, too. Dave from the off-licence told me, "It's the recession. People have stopped smoking 'cos now they know it kills 'em, and they can't afford a drink, only on special occasions."

"Yes. I suppose so. But why have they all stopped knitting and sewing."

He shrugged his shoulders, unable to answer. I knew that people could go to Bromley market and buy haberdashery at a much cheaper price on Thursdays, but now a Sunday market had opened up, too. Jeff and I sat down to discuss how we could help trade. Regretfully, I would have to stop ordering stock, because we would soon be in a position where we wouldn't be able to pay for it. We decided to change the window displays more frequently, and we would have special offers. We also decided to give discount for sales over a certain amount of money. This all helped for a while and as the stock was being depleted Jeff moved the remainder of it to the front of the shop to make it look as though we had lots of it. We also had a closing down sale which lasted nearly a year. The local people came in to buy everything at the sale price whilst voicing their indignation that we were having to close, and telling me how much they were going to miss us. Now that I was not buying stock it gave us a chance to save some money. Jeff also put up a partition and redecorated the back of the shop, giving it to Joe for his own bedroom. He was thrilled about that, as he had always shared his room, initially with Annette and then with Paul, and although it was not ideal because it was downstairs and the room did not have central heating, it suited Joe and made him feel grown-up.

In the spring of 1980, when I had cleared out most of the stock, a man came into the shop to see me.

"I see the shop is looking empty. Would you be interested in letting it out to me? I need an office."

"I'm not sure," was my first reaction. Did we want strangers occupying our shop? I took his name and telephone number, promising to discuss it with Jeff and let him know. So when the children were in bed, and we were alone, I told Jeff about it. He listened to me, musing, "Well my love, we must be realistic. We cannot afford to put stock in the shop, we do not have the money. If we sit tight here for a while, and he pays enough rent to pay the rates and overheads, we may be in a position to sell the shop and accommodation and buy a house."

"A house!" I echoed, "with a garden for the kids."

"Yes! Do you think I like the idea of you running up two flights of stairs every day?"

I hadn't really thought about that. I was used to life being hard work with a large family, but the idea of a house and a garden was lovely. So we agreed to take up the offer from this man, known as Roy, after Jeff had met him and satisfied himself that he was OK. The next day I telephoned him and he came round to see Jeff after he got in from work. They got on well, and so by the following weekend he had installed himself and his wife in there, with numerous telephones, adding machines and a typewriter.

77

The stress of watching the business going downhill was telling on me, and to add to this Paul had started the behavioural problems predicted earlier by the doctor. If he was told that he could not have something he would turn very aggressive, emit a loud scream like a banshee and bite or push the nearest person.

The first time it happened was when we were at a swimming gala. Annette and Amy were both avid swimmers, full of talent. Amy, particularly at five years old, was a very fast swimmer. We had gone along to watch them compete and as Joe was out with a friend that evening it only left Paul to take with us. We were nervous and excited, caught up in the atmosphere of competitiveness, which was apparent, even in children so young. Amy, although only five years old had won the eight years and under breaststroke. She was proudly sporting the club trophy, the first one she had won. Annette, on the other hand, was hoping to win the under thirteen breaststroke and she was bouncing around, unable to contain her excitement and nerves. Whilst we were sitting in the foyer with Paul discussing her chances he completely caught us off guard.

With a glare of great ferocity he rose from his seat, and in a flash lunged at a passer-by, a boy of about his own age. For no apparent reason he pushed him hard, and gave a loud shriek of indignation as though someone had attacked him.

I was aghast, totally unable to cope momentarily! Jeff was straight out of his seat. He slapped Paul's hand hard, said, "No!" and marched him back to the seat, where he sat down, scowling, with his head down.

I was really shaken! My little boy had acted like a monster, in a furious rage, who knows why? Amy dissolved into tears.

"Mummy! I don't like it when Paul does that. He frightens me."

Jeff had tried to catch up with the boy that Paul had pushed but he had run off.

"What can it be that upset him?" I asked, nervously.

"Whatever it is he'll have to learn that he can't behave like that in public, or we'll be banned from everywhere!" remarked Jeff grimly. As if to back his statement the boy appeared, accompanied by a man, obviously his father.

"*He* pushed me, Dad!" pointing accusingly at Paul, who had his head lowered.

Jeff said politely, "I'm really sorry about that. Our son is handicapped and . . ."

"Don't give me any excuses!" the man snarled. "No one pushes *my* son around. If he's got the habits of an animal then keep him locked up or else . . . !"

Jeff's patience snapped. "Don't threaten me! He only pushed him. We're sorry, but he's unpredictable."

"You mean you can't control him!" he sneered.

I could not stand any more of this. The swimming temporarily forgotten, I did the only thing I could think of. I took Paul by the hand and led him outside where we could sit in the quietness of the car and calm down. I remember seeing the tears in Annette's eyes and the distressed faces of both my daughters. I heard afterwards that when she swam her race she did her slowest time ever, and came last!

Chapter Sixteen

We did not take Paul to any more swimming galas, not only did the humid atmosphere upset him, but also it didn't help the girls to swim their best. Also I could not stand the strain of worrying whether he would attack another child. So Jeff and I took it in turns to baby-sit, or sometimes Joe, who was now fourteen and very responsible, would do it. I could see that already as a family we were becoming segregated.

To my horror, Paul's behaviour was becoming more self-destructive. He had now started to pull at his hair when angry, and it came out in clumps. Within a month he was bald! I wept inwardly. What was happening to my son?

I put a little cap on him to try and curb the curious stares when we were out and then took him to the doctor.

"I'm sorry, my dear!" he shook his head after carefully looking at him. "Be prepared! It's a nervous habit that handicapped people have. It may never grow again, unfortunately."

I said, pleadingly, "His beautiful hair! Surely he won't be bald forever!"

I just couldn't bear the thought of it. He looked such a pathetic little boy without his hair, and I was becoming nervous and uncertain of my own son! When angry he could be as quick as lightning, and as I had been kicked when I had refused to give him more food after he had vomited up a meal I was wary. Sadly the girls, particularly Amy, who was smaller than him, were also becoming unsure of him, but he never tried to attack Joe or Jeff.

I couldn't believe that things could get much worse than this for Paul, but I was wrong. To add to his problems he

80

developed a urine infection, which made him frightened to drink fluids. I had to coax him because he was becoming dehydrated, and after a few days I managed to get a little fluid down him. Then he started to starve himself. It was during school holidays and every evening when we sat down to dinner, he would give a howl of rage, and then throw the contents of his plate on the floor. I was so distressed that I couldn't eat either, and by the end of the week we were all nervous wrecks.

The family dinner-table, instead of being a pleasant place to meet for a social interlude, when we all came together at the end of the day, was now turned into a battleground. It seemed to me that Paul was deliberately starving himself to death, and full of fear for what I would be told, I took him to the doctor. He examined him as well as he could, as Paul was angry and unco-operative. As I looked at him, gently feeling his thin fragile little body where he had lost weight, and saw his bald head, with his eyes looking even more huge, flashing with anger, I felt sick inside.

"He has anorexia. I am going to prescribe this tonic medicine. Hopefully it will revive his appetite, but if it hasn't within three days you must bring him back."

I felt a stab of fear in my chest. I didn't feel able to cope with any more worry.

"What will happen if he still won't eat?"

The doctor's voice was determined but kind.

"He will have to go into hospital and be fed through a tube!"

I knew then that my fears were justified, and this was serious. I prayed silently. God, please let me keep my son alive! What can I do to make him eat again? God answered my prayers through Jeff.

When I arrived home and told him what had been said by the doctor he became very determined.

"Right! Today at dinner Paul *will* eat!"

I felt sick inside. I couldn't bear to go through this charade again. It was affecting the rest of us, and I couldn't eat either and knew I was losing weight.

When we sat down later to eat I prayed that this time would be all right. I had cooked minced meat, usually Paul's favourite dinner, just to tempt him.

He gave the now all too familiar howl of rage, bit his wrist ferociously until he drew blood, and went to overturn the plate, but Jeff was too quick for him. In a loud voice he shouted.

"No Paul! Pick up your spoon and eat your dinner!"

Paul ignored him, and the girls started crying.

"Mummy! Why is Paul so angry?" from Amy.

I tried to comfort them, near to tears myself.

Jeff said again, firmly, "Pick up your spoon and eat your dinner!"

We all held our breaths, but Paul kept his head down, retreating back into his own inward world.

Jeff would not be beaten. "Paul, if you ignore me I will take all your cars away from you!"

Paul's only response to this, the worst threat imaginable, was to give Jeff a look of hate.

"OK," said Jeff, "can you all leave the room. I need to talk to Paul on a one to one basis."

I felt so sick, and was glad to escape. One thing I knew about Jeff was that he would not resort to violence. I trusted him with Paul implicitly. We all waited uneasily in the other room.

After about five minutes Jeff called us back and said triumphantly, "Well, he's had about half of what you gave him. At least it's a start. Good boy, Paul!"

I was amazed. "How did you do it?"

Jeff grinned. "I'll tell you later, but right now Paul you can get down and play with your cars whilst *we* all have *our* dinner." Paul stumbled down from the table to seek the familiar refuge of his bean bag on the floor. He sat there content to retreat into his own world again.

I looked at this husband of mine, so strong, tough and unyielding when necessary, and I wondered for the umpteenth time how I would ever have been able to manage Paul without him.

It took about a week for Paul to regain his appetite, encouraged by Jeff's firmness at meal-times. The battle of wills had been fought and won. The result of this was that Jeff had earnt a grudging respect from Paul. Paul had met his match and found someone with a stronger will who could control him, and would not tolerate his violent behaviour.

Chapter Seventeen

I found out afterwards that Jeff had held Paul's nose to make him open his mouth to get the food in. He had done it three times before Paul had stopped spitting it out. Jeff assured me that it was not a pretty sight, and he was glad I was not in the room to see Paul, who was obviously very angry. Anyway it worked! Paul stopped looking so fragile and put on some weight. I have never understood to this day why he starved himself like that, as eating has always been one of his most pleasurable habits. I felt sad that, locked inside his little world, in the recesses of his mind was a reason for his behaviour that he could never be able to convey to us. We had noticed, over the years, that Paul had a great deal of intelligence and understanding of what we say. Is it any wonder that he became aggressive when we didn't understand what was wrong with him and by a cruel accident of nature he was not able to tell us?

Paul was eating properly at school now as well, and to our tremendous relief his hair was growing back again. It was a darker blond now. He had lost that lovely silver blond colour, which is associated with early childhood, but it was thick and wavy and he stopped tugging at it when he became angry.

Now that Roy and his entourage were in the shop it left me relatively free during the day. We had discussed the possibility of a day job for me, but it was difficult with Paul. Sometimes he couldn't go to school because he was unwell and then there were holidays. Joe and Annette did a lot of baby-sitting then if needed, but I felt guilty about it. Amy, too, as she was only five, needed to be met from school and looked after. Joe didn't get home in time to help and Annette

84

went straight from school to her swimming training every night.

We had stopped working in the evenings now, but I needed a day job so that we could save towards buying a house. But who would employ me with all my problems?

Jeff saw a job advertised in a local china and glass shop, situated only a mile away. My first reaction was negative.

"I couldn't work there. I might break things. Anyway, what about Paul and Amy?"

Annie was sitting drinking tea with us. "I've got the solution," glancing at Jeff for support. "I need a little job to occupy my afternoons. I can meet Amy, come back here, collect Paul from his coach and give them tea."

Jeff joined in. "Wonderful, Annie! I'll be in at five o'clock to take over, or Joe will, whoever is first, and then you can go home."

It seemed like a 'fait accompli' but they made me feel that I wasn't so tied, and therefore would be able to keep a job down.

"Thanks, Annie." I still felt dubious. "Of course I'll be glad to pay you, but what about Paul's tempers?"

"He won't have any with me!" she laughed, and I knew she was probably right. Apart from the fact that Paul knew she had a lot of affection for him, there was also something about her larger than life personality that kept his temper at bay. She was tall and purposeful, and he also knew that she understood him well. I had no doubt in my mind that she could handle him.

"It's for three days a week, working every other Saturday, but first I have to get the job!" I reminded them. "The fact that our business has gone down the tubes might not put me in a favourable light."

"Rubbish!" retorted Jeff, hotly. "You can't help a recession. You've got the experience they're looking for."

So I telephoned the shop and spoke to the manager, and he arranged an interview for the next day. I went for my interview with great trepidation. Not only did I badly want the job, but also I needed a break from Paul sometimes. His unpredictable outbursts were wearing me down and I felt I needed the company of others, away from the home

85

environment. The shop was situated half way down the high street, and was divided into two units. One housed china and glass, and a variety of selective giftware by leading manufacturers, and the other unit had light fittings and shades. The manager took me into his office and interviewed me, and then he asked me about our shop, what had I been doing and for how long. The usual sort of questions. I explained how the business had died. He was not surprised.

"Well, it's the recession! We've been lucky, and so far managed to survive," he grimaced.

Maybe it wasn't going against me too much. He looked down at my application form. "I see you have four children. What happens during holiday times? I see that two of them are under ten years."

I drew a deep breath. May God forgive me if I told a white lie. I needed the job! I heard my voice saying, "My husband works at night and is at home a lot during the day, but failing that I have a very good friend who helps out."

"Splendid! When can you start?"

I stared at him quite taken aback. Was it really so easy?

"Well, tomorrow I think."

He laughed. "No! I think you deserve a day's notice. Let's make it on Wednesday. Come in the shop and meet the staff."

I followed him out onto the shop floor, and he introduced me to Ena, a lady who worked full-time, and had been there for many years. There was also Paula, another lady with a grown-up family who also worked three days a week. Over in the lighting department was Linda, a very lively character, and Alison who must have been easily forty-five if she was a day but was sporting a mini-skirt, had hair like Brigitte Bardot and legs that would have looked better if she'd worn tights. I found out later that she was a bit eccentric.

When I got home I told Jeff about the way I had misled the manager, and that I had also got the job. "You had to. You wouldn't have got the job. We'll make sure that you're reliable, so don't worry."

I was still doubtful. "But what about holidays? It will fall on Joe and Annette. Will Annie help all day sometimes?"

"I don't know, love, but we'll cross that bridge when we

come to it. All we can do is to live from day to day, and take each day as it comes."

So I started my job and I really was enjoying it. I didn't tell anyone about Paul, only saying that I had four children, and their ages. The 'girls' I worked with were quite amusing, especially Alison, who made a beeline for any male under eighty except her husband. There was a certain amount of bitching, as you would expect from women working together, but generally speaking we all got on well. I was so anxious to please that I really tried hard at my job. In the mornings, whilst I was waiting for Paul's coach to come and pick him up for school, I prayed it would not be late. If I was late I would not have known what explanation to give. So far I had been lucky, and in my third week I started to relax a little more and worry less. Things seemed to be working out.

During the afternoon, Leslie, our manager, took me into the lighting department to familiarise me so that I could work in there, too, if needed. He pointed out some of the crystal chandeliers, and then excused himself when a telephone call came in for him. Paula came up to talk to me, and as I looked up at a very impressive chandelier something strange happened to me. I felt dizzy. For the first time in my life I felt as if I was going to faint! I tried to fight it. This was the last thing I could afford to happen. I had only just started this job. No way could I be off sick! Paula was talking but I wasn't taking in what she was saying. I was really struggling to fight this dizziness. I suddenly felt as if I was dying. A terrible fear wrapped itself around me, and my voice, as if from afar, whispered. "I think I'm going to faint."

The next thing that I remember is sitting on a chair in the stock room, with Paula bending over me, her motherly face full of concern.

"Are you all right now, dear? You did go white! What happened?"

I was confused, and I couldn't remember. She reminded me.

"You felt faint and you lost your colour, so I brought you out here, away from anything breakable."

"I can't understand it. I'm not a person who faints."

"Don't worry about it. It's hot in the lighting, and never

look up at chandeliers. They can make you feel disorientated."

I could only assume that this was what had caused my dizziness, and to my extreme embarrassment Leslie came out to see what had happened. Paula explained, and I felt rather ridiculous sitting there on the chair.

"Well, Carrie, it's five o'clock, go home a little early tonight," he said kindly.

I opened my mouth to protest but Paula cut in, "Good idea! There's nothing much happening, and then you'll feel better for Saturday when we will be busy."

It seemed pointless to argue, so I thanked Leslie, and assured him that I would be fit by Saturday.

When I arrived home Jeff was surprised to see me early, and I explained what had happened. We both put it down to the heat and the glare of the lights in the shop.

I returned to work on Saturday in good spirits and feeling fine. We had a very busy day and I served a lot of customers. I was beginning to know the stock now, and Jeff was at home with the children, so I knew all would be well. When I came home, tired but elated, I found Joe and Annette had prepared tea and given it to Paul and Amy. They were all eating spaghetti and listening to a radio, on loudly in the kitchen. I didn't mind if they were happy, and Jeff and I sat down and had a cup of tea together in the lounge.

We swopped news with each other about what we had been doing during the day. Suddenly, whilst Jeff was talking, I felt a feeling of fear pass through me. I went to take a deep breath, and the most peculiar thing happened. I couldn't breathe! I was not in pain but I was struggling to breathe. I felt as if I was sinking . . . dying! God help me. My face must have changed colour because Jeff said, "Carrie! What's wrong for God's sake?"

"Help!" I gasped, "I'm dying!" and then came merciful oblivion.

Chapter Eighteen

When I came to I was lying under the quilt in our bed. Jeff was holding my hand and Annie was there, too. I heard him say, "A stroke . . . Oh no, Carrie love, not you, you're my life."

Then Annie, strong, firm and sensible. "It might not be, just because the symptoms are similar. She's only thirty-six! Anyway, the doctor will be here soon . . . "

I *was* dying then. Is this what it's like when everyone talks about you but not to you? Even in my feeble state I wondered what would happen to my children, especially Paul. Then the doctor was there, a kindly elderly man. He gently made me sit up.

"I'm dying!" I heard myself say.

"No, you're not my dear." He smiled. "A healthy lady like you with four lovely children and such a good husband."

"But I can't breathe! I feel dizzy! I fainted! Why?"

I felt breathless again and agitated. I felt that he didn't understand. He calmly examined me thoroughly, tested my heart, lungs and blood pressure, looked in my ears and down my throat. When he had finished he sat down at the end of the bed, which had been tactfully vacated by Jeff and Annie.

"You are suffering from stress, my dear, and are very close to having a nervous breakdown."

"Stress! But I've always had stress and I can cope with it. This is something physically wrong."

"No. It's your mind that is causing your body to play up. Your brain is saying give me a break. The inability to breathe is called a panic attack. I can give you some pills to take, but you must try and relax more and not get too tired physically.

That doesn't help. Come to my surgery in a week."

He wrote me out a prescription and then called Jeff in. He reiterated what he had told me, but when Jeff asked about my job, he said, "I think it would be good for your wife to carry on with it. It will help keep her mind occupied, but after she is better. She needs a few days off."

So Jeff had the job of telephoning and explaining that I was ill. To me this was the worst thing that could have happened after only three weeks of working there, and I really expected to lose my job, but he told Leslie that I was suffering from 'flu.

After three days I returned to work and then I went through a year of hell! Because of my job I managed to keep my sanity. The one thing I was determined to do was not to lose it. So I went to great lengths to hide my disability. I did not understand what was happening to me. I was obsessed with the idea that I was going mad or dying! I really went to hell and back to many times! Anyone who has experienced similar feelings will know what I mean, and all the time I tried hard to fight it and control what was happening to me.

First of all I became convinced that my left arm would not stop shaking and I could not keep it still. I went to see the doctor and he examined me, assuring me that nothing was wrong. Then I had a pain in the other arm, and I thought that it was paralysed. Once again I went to see him.

Next was my neck. I felt as if someone was trying to choke me to death. I was tested to see if my thyroid gland was working normally, and it was.

Then I developed agoraphobia. When we were in a crowded room, I suddenly had to leave it because I had to be alone. I was also frightened of going outside the house. I couldn't understand what was happening to me. Finally, to cap it all, I lost the ability to go shopping, a very necessary part of my life. I fainted in the local supermarket whilst trying to do my shopping, and then one day when I had taken Annette and Amy shopping with me in Bromley the same thing happened to me in a clothes store. The kind shop assistant sat outside with me on a chair and waited whilst Annette telephoned for Jeff to come and get me. When he arrived he was not sympathetic.

"I can't run all round Bromley after you and your crazy hang-ups!"

I sobbed. How could he be so cruel! He didn't know the hell I was going through! I didn't *want* to be like this. God knows how it was affecting the kids!

Joe and Annette had virtually taken over looking after Paul, except at night. I couldn't sleep and I stumbled out of bed to settle him whilst everyone else slept. How I kept my job through all of this I really don't know. I made mistakes and forgot things. I got told off, but I never admitted that I was ill.

I had been visiting the doctor regularly, accompanied by Jeff, ever since my first 'panic attack', but he was not happy with my progress. The doctor as ever was sympathetic. "You have had quite a life, my dear. You have four children, which would be more than enough for some people, but you also have all the stress involved in caring for Paul. You have also suffered a broken marriage, and a shattering of self morale. No wonder it has all caught up on you. I wonder how you've managed to cope as long as you have!"

"I feel so ashamed that I can't cope, doctor. I try so hard!" I flashed a look of self-reproach at Jeff, who as usual was firm and unyielding.

"I am increasing your tranquillisers to one twice a day to see if that helps you to stay calm, and then come back and see me in a month." He paused, "I have written to 'The Cedars', our local hospital housing handicapped children, asking if Paul can have respite care some weekends to give the whole family a break. I am also arranging for a home help to come during the holidays to look after the two younger children so that you can keep your job going."

This news took a great deal of worry off my mind. Baby-sitting had so far fallen onto Joe and Annette, and this had made me feel guilty because I knew that they were missing out on the normal pursuits of freedom that they were entitled to at their age.

There had been one occasion when they had taken Paul and Amy to our local park for the afternoon. When they arrived home they were very upset and angry. Amy had explained.

"Paul was playing on the little slide whilst Joe was pushing me on the swing. When he got off the slide some boys pushed his head under the water fountain and soaked him!"

From what I could gather Annette had been taken by surprise because Paul's curiosity had been aroused by seeing the water gushing out of the water fountain. The two boys, seeing him run over whooping with excitement, had realised he was retarded and thought it was great fun to force his head under to try and frighten him. Amy had screamed angrily at them, but luckily Paul was not hurt, so Joe and Annette had acted with as much dignity as they could. They simply removed Amy and Paul from the situation and came home, which was the best move possible. So if there was someone else around whilst I was at work it would certainly ease the burden.

So I stepped up my tranquillisers as suggested by the doctor, and gradually I felt more relaxed. Things were not bothering me so acutely now.

This was just as well, because I knew that Jeff was fed up with it, and so was I! I was surprised that he hadn't left me and all my problems before now. I wasn't exactly a ray of sunshine to live with.

One morning he was watching me as I took my pill. It did help to control my feelings of panic and now the attacks were occurring less frequently. Jeff spoke to me accusingly, "How can you be so weak, propping yourself up through life with pills?"

"But Dr Sherrat prescribed them!" I felt hurt.

"I don't care! You should have the guts to get along without them. What sort of example is it to the kids?"

I felt miserable. He was tough and I was a failure. I was sure he didn't love me. I burst out defensively, "OK, I never was a good marriage prospect, and now you regret taking me on with all my problems, I know."

"Do you?" he said smoothly. "*Your* problems, as you call them, are mine, too, but I didn't think that you lacked guts!"

I ran weeping from the room. I felt as if the whole world was against me and I was about to lose everything. Even Joe and Annette seemed to be avoiding me.

I went to the doctor again, alone, and told him what had

happened.

"Well, Mrs Carter, I can assure you that your husband does love you dearly, and admires you, too. He is probably using tough measures to help you because he thinks it might be more effective than sympathy."

I said desperately, "I must get off these pills!"

"It's up to you, it always has been really, but rest assured that the small dose that you have is not addictive. Don't lose heart. You are strong enough to see this through, I know. Your husband is really proud of you. He has always admired the way that you have coped with Paul."

I felt a stab of remorse inside. I was letting everyone down, especially myself! I vowed that I would go on fighting these panics and fears without pills and I would win!

So, for the next year, every time I felt an attack come on I just told myself I wasn't dying and that it was only stress, and it worked. I started being able to cope again. Paul spent some weekends at 'The Cedars', every other weekend with his dad, still, and Jeff and I took Amy out on the weekends that she was on her own. Within a month I had weaned myself off the tranquillisers, and my relationship with Jeff was better because I had regained my self-respect. I was determined that he would not look down on me for being weak!

Chapter Nineteen

It was easily a year before I could get myself together again, but once I did life became a lot easier. I was learning, as we all were, to laugh more and be happy. I needed to have a sense of humour in bringing up Paul! His favourite trick was to use his plate as a flying saucer when he had eaten as much as he wanted. As we ducked to avoid the missile, we watched with a mixture of horror and amusement as baked beans or spaghetti remains dripped despondently down the kitchen wall. Annie, with her usual sense of humour, roared with laughter one day as Paul decided that he didn't want a drink. I was sitting chatting to her, and in a bid to get my attention he hurled his cup in my direction. It whistled past, just missing my ear, striking the arm of the chair. The sticky fruit juice ran effortlessly down the chair onto my lap, covering my skirt and blouse rapidly. I exclaimed, "Oh! I don't think he wanted that."

"The understatement of the year, surely?" chortled Annie.

Naturally, we had to let him realise that he couldn't behave like that, but nevertheless it provided amusing entertainment at times. He also developed a habit of twirling round in a circle every so often when we were out, and this could prove a problem in the middle of a crowded supermarket. On one occasion he successfully managed to knock a completed display of tinned peas on to the floor. The next week, when we went in, I noticed they were stacked in a trolley marked, 'DENTED TINS AT HALF PRICE'. This time I made sure that he kept a low profile by sitting in the shopping trolley.

94

In 1981, much to our delight, Annie remarried. There was one snag from our point of view. The child minding had to stop as they were buying a house and she needed to return to work full-time to help to pay the mortgage. So we advertised for a baby-sitter 'with patience' and we got Denise! I felt a bit doubtful about her when she came, but I decided to give her a chance. She brought her three-year-old daughter with her (not that I minded that at all), and then proceeded to cook her a meal containing all that she could find in the fridge. She gave Paul and Amy bread and jam, and when Amy complained, she said briskly, "You and Paul have had dinner at school. Lisa is hungry!"

Amy grumbled to me when I got home, saying indignantly, "I couldn't even watch my programme. We had to have a baby programme that Lisa wanted."

"You must learn to give in gracefully to younger children, Amy. You can't always have what you want."

As the youngest Amy was used to getting her own way, too. I didn't think it would harm her to be unselfish.

About a week later I came home to be greeted by an enraged Denise. "Look!" She rolled up her sleeve to display teeth marks, guess whose? "He's a monster! He won't take 'no' for an answer, and so he bit me!"

Paul had his head down. He knew he had done wrong. I sent him in to his bedroom, and then came back to calm down Denise.

"Why did he do this, Denise?"

"He wanted ice-cream and I told him 'no'!"

"That's not fair!" Amy burst in fiercely, unable to contain herself any longer. "Denise gave the ice-cream to Lisa. There wasn't any left for Paul and I. He brought the empty box over to me."

I had a mental picture of what had happened. Paul had learnt to fetch the ice-cream from the freezer whenever he wanted it. We all praised him highly for so clearly making his needs known to us. I could imagine his anger when the ice-cream had been given only to Lisa.

Denise went, never to return, and once again we advertised for a baby-sitter. Muriel was the next one. She looked weird, not at all how you would picture a baby-sitter, but she liked

Paul and he seemed to like her. He never tried to attack her. One day she called in at the shop to borrow my key because she had left hers at home, and I was amazed to see her sporting a black leather jacket with chains dangling from it, much to the amusement of my work colleagues. Her explanation was that it belonged to her nephew and he had lent it to her because she was cold.

At work there had been a few changes of staff by 1982, and I was still hanging on to my job. I had been there for two years and was considered reliable, but only because Jeff had come to my rescue several times when Paul was ill on a day when I was due to work. He simply telephoned in and booked a day's annual leave at short notice. Once I had been telephoned at work to go and collect Paul from school because he wasn't well, but I managed to cover up by using my lunch hour to do it, and then was lucky enough to get Muriel to come a bit earlier to hold the fort until Jeff got in. We lived from day to day, not looking too hard into the future.

Roy had decided, after two years, to look for larger premises to rent. He vacated the shop, so now seemed the right time to sell. We put our shop and maisonette on the market and found a buyer immediately. My Hooker, our buyer, was an estate agent, and he planned to run the office from there and let the maisonette out. I took an instant dislike to him at first sight. He was small, but what he lacked in height he made up for verbally. He tried to organise our lives completely. We took no notice, all he was buying was our property, and once his deposit was paid we went to find a house. We chose one situated within a mile away in a pretty tree-lined road. We planned to have an extension built to provide three extra bedrooms, one each for the children.

Moving day was exciting for all of us. It was lovely to have a house with a garden, and Joe had volunteered to take a day off school to help Jeff with the moving of the furniture, as we had hired our own van. He was now sixteen and quite useful for lifting heavy things. Initially we were very cramped for space. The children all had to share the two bedrooms whilst Jeff and I turned the lounge into our bedroom, but eventually planning permission was passed for our extension to be built.

Then the next shock came. When we contacted the builder who had supplied the estimate, he told us that he had underestimated, and that the cost would be £5,000 more than he had originally thought. This really put a damp squib on things! I was fed up with trying to cope in such cramped conditions, and the children were, too. Although we had borrowed extra money to finance the extension it would not now be enough, and most of our savings had gone on legal fees, surveys, etc. Jeff made a decision.

"I'm going to do it myself. I know how."

I was very dubious. Decorating was one thing, building was quite another! However, there seemed to be no alternative, and I hated feeling as if we were continually in a mess.

So we didn't have a holiday. Instead Jeff took two weeks off work and built the extension. He added an extra piece all the way along the end of the house and also built two more rooms above the kitchen. A representative from our local council came round periodically to check that everything was being done properly and 'pass it'. Jeff was glad of this and so was I. When it was finished, not only did it make our bedroom and lounge larger, it also provided us with five bedrooms, which meant that everyone had their own room, much to the children's great delight.

The bedrooms were small but compact, with fitted wardrobes, and Joe had a shaver socket and light. He had just started shaving and felt grown up. Amy had the smallest room, and she had the bunk bed with a wardrobe and dressing table unit built underneath to give her more space. Paul's room was ideal for him, and I hoped that once he was on his own he would sleep more soundly. Sometimes he would lay awake for hours, laughing and making baby sounds to himself. But his sleep pattern was rather erratic. Occasionally he would fall asleep in the afternoon and often he was loth to wake up early in the morning. I allowed him to sleep in for the morning on Saturdays and Sundays, but during the week he had to be up for school. Breakfast was a meal he really enjoyed, and once he had eaten that he was far more co-operative. He was now attempting to dress and undress himself with a little prompting, and this was another pleasing

97

step forward. The only time he forgot to undress was on the beach before going in the water, if I wasn't quick enough to stop him. I learnt this to my cost on a day out! Luckily it was warm because he had to come home in the car in his swimming trunks.

My dad had remarried by now and I found my stepmother, Bessie, easy to get along with. I still missed my mother, I always would of course, but one had to learn to adjust. And I was pleased that someone was there to share the later years of his life with him because I knew that my mother's death had left a terrible void in his life.

Joe left school in the summer of 1982 and went on to college for a year of further studies. Annette was still swimming, she was now aged fourteen and had also become a very promising long distance runner, and had joined a local running club to further this talent. Amy, too, had blossomed into an outstanding swimmer, and she went to galas all over the south-east of England, bringing home medals and trophies as a result of her efforts. Jeff and I were not able to go out together much, but if Joe or Annette were free they would baby-sit for Paul so that we could both go and watch her swim.

Paul's development did not change very much until 1984, when he reached puberty. It was my fortieth birthday, not the sort of age one can forget, and it was Sunday. We had just finished our dinner and everyone was jolly. Jeff had opened a bottle of wine to celebrate and we were feeling mellow. We were playing a tape and the music was pulsating with a loud beat. Paul was happy. He loved music, and he got out of his chair giggling, wanting to collect up the empty pudding plates.

"Go on Paul, good boy," urged Jeff.

Paul laughed with happiness, and I noticed him stretching out his hands to pick up the bowls. Then his hands seemed to twitch and he lost control of himself. I watched, horrified and totally unable to move as he gave a loud cry of anguish and fell down, dragging the cloth and table contents with him. He lay on the floor, writhing and making choking noises. Jeff and I ran to help him. He lay still now having lost consciousness.

"Move his head to the side so that he can breathe," ordered Jeff.

I obeyed silently. My inside was full of churning emotions. Fear, misery and heartbreak for my son who seemed to have been given more than his fair share of handicaps to contend with already, and now this! I wanted to shout and scream and berate the injustice of it. I did not need to be told that Paul had suffered his first epileptic fit.

Chapter Twenty

By the time the doctor had arrived Paul had recovered.
He was sitting on the floor, obviously bewildered and dazed.
The doctor examined Paul gently whilst Paul stared at
him. His blue eyes looked cloudy and his response to the
doctor's handling of him was very passive. He was not our
usual doctor because at the weekend there was only an
emergency call out, so he asked for a few more details.

"Has this happened before?"

"No." I shook my head. I was inwardly thinking. Why?
Hasn't he had enough problems? It didn't seem fair.

"He is probably feeling grotty now, with a headache, but
he won't remember what happened."

"Should I put him to bed, doctor?" I enquired, anxiously.

"If he wants to go. This is not serious. As with all brain
damaged children, epileptic fits will occur sometimes. As
he has reached thirteen without one before you are lucky.
He will probably only have one occasionally."

Lucky! I thought. What's lucky about it! Still I mustn't
be bitter about it. At least we have him. We've loved him and
cared for him for so long between us that it creates a bond
that can never be broken. My Jekyll and Hyde son! One
minute smiling and happy, at the next he can change into a
monster in a fury! But right now he was a docile little lamb
who needed our help. I tried to tuck him on to the settee to
rest. It seemed cruel to put him to bed as if he had been
naughty. But, with his usual indomitable will, he got off the
settee to go and look for his cars. I think they have always
represented some sort of emotional security to him. I've
noticed in times of stress he seems to derive comfort by

holding one in his hand.

Joe, Annette and Amy were not as shaken by this latest development as I expected them to be. They were growing up to be resilient and stoic, and they had carried on with the washing-up and clearing the dishes whilst the doctor was here. They took the news without much comment, and seemed to accept it unquestioningly. Jeff didn't say much either, almost as if he had been expecting it. I felt the now all too familiar pang of heartache inside, but I knew the best way that I could help Paul was to squash it down and make the best of things.

The doctor was right. Paul's epileptic fits, although distressing to see, were only occasional, maybe one every three months. He was usually a little sleepy and subdued afterwards, but other than that there were no apparent ill effects.

However, later that same year his asthma seemed to worsen, and in the first week of December he had a bad attack and was admitted to hospital. I couldn't bear to see him fighting for breath, his lips pale and bloodless, and his colour grey. I really thought he was dying!

When he was admitted to hospital he was put on a machine called a nebuliser. It puffed Ventolin spray into his mouth and nose via a mask, and I was amazed to see his colour return to normal after only five minutes of this treatment. Then, joy of joys, he gave me his radiant smile, which means all is well with him, and I hugged him to me, relief flooding through my inside. Every frightening episode over the years has only served to make him more precious to me, and it never ceases to amaze me the courage and will to live that he has in spite of all his handicaps. One smile from Paul somehow makes everything worthwhile!

On the second day of his stay, when I arrived to see him, I was told by the doctor that he wanted to speak to me. As always I waited with trepidation, unsure of what I would be told. The doctor entered the room, smiling. It seemed that I needn't have worried.

"Paul is certainly determined not to waste time being ill for long! You can take him home now, his breathing is stable and he is eating well."

"That is good news, doctor! He gave us a fright yesterday!"

"The biggest problem with Paul is that he cannot speak, and when breathing is difficult he panics. It then becomes a vicious circle and it develops into a full blown asthma attack."

I nodded. This was what I had thought. I volunteered. "He has speech therapy at school, and we try to encourage him at home, doctor, but we only get sounds."

"Yes," he sighed. "Some children like Paul with autistic tendencies learn to speak but the majority of them never do."

"What can we do to help him?"

"Well, so that he doesn't need to come into hospital every time he gets wheezy, we are going to issue you with a nebuliser to keep at home, but only give it to him when absolutely necessary. We don't want him to become dependent on it."

He went on to explain that as Paul did not seem to understand about using an inhaler on a regular basis (we couldn't get him to breathe in deeply) this could be the answer. He also explained that we would need to return the machine every six months for it to be serviced, but this would coincide with Paul's check ups with the paediatrician.

So Paul and I left the hospital with a nebuliser. It did save the day on occasions and he didn't need to go to hospital, but I noticed to my dismay that his wheezing was becoming more frequent. I had been warned that puberty, with hormonal changes which Paul couldn't understand, was a major contributor towards this, so I tried not to get too alarmed. Without the nebuliser he would hardly have been at school that winter, and some mornings I felt so guilty after nebulising him and putting him on the coach for school. I went to work worrying and wondering whether he would be all right.

In the spring of 1985 his health picked up again, and once more things became a little easier. Several things happened around that time, all quite pleasing. Joe and Annette were both working and contributing towards their keep, and Jeff had been given promotion at work and a pay rise. Money was no longer a problem, or lack of it! We were beginning to have a comfortable way of life and it looked as if our struggling days were over.

Both of the girls had turned out to be very talented at sports. Annette had now moved on to running, and had been part of the relay team that had broken the British record. On the strength of this they were presented to the mayor, and made the local paper's sports headlines. This fired her enthusiasm even more. She was now working in a bank, and running for them, too. She was saving hard because she wanted to go to a summer camp in America in the hopes of furthering her ambitions there.

Amy was now the Kent champion for breaststroke, and next year she would be old enough to compete at national level, so all in all life was very exciting for us.

In the spring of 1985, after a succession of managers in our shop, the latest one left, and the managing director came over to see me. This was Leslie, the manager who had taken me on before he had got promotion. He called me in to the office and I went in wondering what could be wrong.

"Well, Carrie, how would you feel about being the manager of this branch?"

Chapter Twenty-one

I stared at Leslie, dumbfounded. Me? I had always got on with my job quietly, believing no one ever noticed me. Obviously I felt flattered, but other thoughts were running through my mind. A manager worked full-time. Could I hold a full-time job down and cope with Paul? Although the girls I worked with knew by now, none of our company directors did. Thanks to a concerted team effort from the family I had managed to cope, but working five days a week was another thing.

"You've been here for five years, Carrie. You know the customers and the job. We have discussed it at head office and feel that you would be right for the job."

I gulped. If only I was free to make a decision. "Thank you, Leslie, for asking me. I have to discuss it with Jeff."

"Of course, I understand. But will you let me know soon?"

"I'll let you know tomorrow."

He then explained my extra duties and the salary that I would get, with one week day off of my choice. After he had gone I spent the afternoon turning it over in my mind. I knew that if I didn't take it there would be other people from the company applying. Managership was a much coveted job, and I could end up with someone in charge of me who was less experienced than I was, and I didn't fancy that. The extra money would be a plus, also the status and the opportunity to direct staff and improve shop takings.

Unfortunately, there were lots of things on the minus side. Longer hours for me to work. Could I dare hope that Paul's health would stay stable? Was I being unfair to my husband and family by working longer hours? Money was not everything and our financial situation was more comfortable now. Jeff no longer had to maintain his daughters from his first marriage. They were now at work and he had paid up the mortgage on the home from his first marriage, too.

When I went home that evening and told everyone, the reaction was unanimous. Jeff listened to me, whilst beaming with pleasure. He remarked, "I don't know why they didn't ask you before. All those young kids they had as managers! It's your decision, but I'll be proud of you if you take it."

"Well done, Mum!"

I looked at them all. Had they forgotten? What about Paul?

"Suppose Paul isn't well. We must take that possibility into consideration."

"Take a chance, love. We've got through the last five years, somehow."

I knew that Jeff was right. I really wanted this job. I had to try. We now had a child minder provided by the home help service, so that was all right. During the long summer holidays a playschool scheme operated, and Paul was picked up from the door at eight-thirty in the morning, and dropped back home at five o'clock. He also had an annual holiday for two weeks at Hastings once a year, provided by the social services, as well as respite care once a month. This was as free as I could be after many years, so I had to take this opportunity.

When I arrived at work the next day I telephoned Leslie and told him of my decision. He seemed pleased.

"That is good news! Now that you've told me I'll let it be known."

"Thanks, Leslie, for everything."

I always felt that he had something to do with my promotion. I remembered back to when I had first started there and come close to a breakdown. He must have noticed something amiss, but he had always been very tactful. Even now, in moments of great stress I could feel panic at times, but I had learnt the knack of fighting it.

So I took on my new job with zest and enthusiasm. Initially there was jealousy and balkiness from one of my colleagues, but I weathered it and it passed. The shop had become rather sloppy under the control of the previous manager, a boy of nineteen, who was more interested in his social life than his job. I took on new staff and set new rules, and within six months our weekly takings were on the up.

At home I was coping. The weekends that Paul was in respite care, or with his dad, found me with Jeff watching Amy swim. This took up a great deal of our spare time and it was exciting to go and watch her compete.

Paul had shot up in height over the past year. Before he had always been very small for his age, but now, at fourteen, he was five feet four inches tall, only about an inch less than me. On one of his visits to the hospital the paediatrician noticed that he was stooping when he walked.

"This young man is getting very round shouldered. We must do something about it!"

So they tried exercises at school, and we did them at home, but Paul continued to stoop. The next time that we were at the hospital the specialist took X-rays of Paul's back, and we were called back for the results. Mr Kiro looked at me and put down his pen, which was poised in mid-air.

"I'm afraid Paul's spine is becoming more crooked as he grows. We cannot perform surgery because he will need to be in plaster for six months and it will badly affect his breathing."

I stared at him, trying to accept this new problem, and I felt the familiar pain of heartache inside again.

His voice became brighter. "However, we are going to measure up Paul for a brace, which will help to hold him upright during puberty whilst he grows."

"Will he be all right?" I asked miserably.

"Of course! We'll take great care of him, but I need to refer you to another hospital because making up the brace is a specialist job."

So Paul and I spent one day a week, which had to be my day off, traipsing backwards and forwards to a London hospital for the next six months. He was measured, then his measurements were checked. Then we received a letter to say that they had mislaid his measurements, so we returned to go through the whole process again. I waited patiently, but with reservations, for his brace. A distinct little hump was forming on his back, and I felt a wave of hurt pass through me every time I noticed it.

One day I received a letter calling us back to the hospital and it stated that Paul's brace was ready. When we got there, to my extreme surprise, I was told that he was not having a brace. "Doctor has decided that it will do more harm than good. It will affect his breathing."

At this point I'm afraid, my patience snapped.

"So you mean to tell me that we have spent the last six months coming backwards and forwards for nothing! Don't you think I have other things to do on my day off?"

The doctor shrugged, evasively, "I'm sorry, but it was *your* paediatrician's decision."

So Paul and I went back to see Mr Kiro, and he apologised profusely, explaining that after a lot of deliberation he had thought that the brace would do more harm than good. What I couldn't understand was why it had taken him six months to arrive at this decision, and why he changed his mind and I was never told.

It was decided once again that we should try exercises and encourage Paul to hold himself upright. This has always been difficult and over the years his stooping, sadly, has increased. When he is shy, or wishes to withdraw from contact with others, he bends his head and shoulders right over, and I realise now that it is all part of his handicapped condition.

After these months of uncertainty we needed something to be happy about, so we were delighted to hear that Amy's swimming had now reached national standard, and she had qualified to swim the breaststroke competition being held at Leeds. We both wanted to go and watch her, it was quite an achievement just to get there and we were very proud.

Jeff had recently bought a van and converted it to a camper, and he was itching to try it out.

"If we both go, we need to take Paul," I reminded him.

"Let's take Paul! We won't make the mistake of taking him in the pool to watch. If the camper's right outside in the car park we can leave him for five minutes."

It wasn't ideal, but it was all we could do, so we set off in the usual state of excitement. I sometimes suffered pangs of guilt about my other children. Over the years I hadn't had much time to give to them. I was always so busy with Paul in one way or another. It was crucial to me not to miss out on this important day for Amy.

We arrived at Leeds and parked the van in the car park. I stayed with Paul whilst Jeff took Amy over to join the others. She wasn't swimming until the next day, but she had to train. She was part of a relay team that had been tipped to win a gold medal.

I sat in the camper with Paul. He drank a glass of orange thirstily with his eyes on me because I had the biscuit tin in my hand. I opened it and he excitedly dipped his hand in, trembling with pleasure.

"One only," I remonstrated, as he brought out as many as his hand could hold, beaming with delight.

"One for Mummy."

He obeyed. It had taken a very long time to get him to share, but he knew. I retrieved the rest of the biscuits and compromised, letting him have one more when he surrendered them without a display of temper. I was wary of Paul's tempers. He was as tall as me now and had amazing strength when angry. But right now he was in a happy mood, obviously enjoying this new adventure. I switched on our portable TV and sat at the table with him watching it. After about an hour Jeff and Amy returned with fish and chips, which we all ate and enjoyed, and then Jeff suggested a walk before bed.

I was curious to have a look around, but wary about taking Paul for a walk. He was going through a very balky phase about walking, and would sometimes put on an attack of wheezing just so that he didn't have to go out. The social services had provided me with an adult size buggy to push him around in but I was loth to use it. After all, his legs were not spastic, and I didn't want to encourage him to be lazy. But what I was doing was worse really. I just wasn't taking him out anywhere.

"There's no reason why Paul can't go for a short walk," said Jeff, "the air will do him good."

I agreed with this, but I was so keyed up about Amy's swim the next day I just didn't want anything to go wrong.

A display of aggression from Paul would unnerve her, I thought. Then I remonstrated with myself not to get paranoid. So we went for a short walk, Amy skipping ahead, chatting excitedly to her dad. Paul and I walked behind. He could not walk far or fast, but he looped his arm through mine. I felt a little tense. I could sense his reluctance, and his face was not relaxed and happy. We walked along a boulevard of shops, stopping to look in the windows. There was the usual type of things, fashions and shoes in the big department store. The willowy models stood nonchalantly, clad in mini-skirts and bright colours, looking just like real people. The brightness seemed to attract Paul and he gazed with rapt attention at the bright window lights, now on. After a while I realised that he was quite enjoying himself. I started to relax and share his enjoyment of the scene. Things that pleased Paul pleased me!

Amy had found a window with sports gear and swimming costumes displayed, and I could hear her trying to coax Jeff. "Daddy, will you buy me that costume?" Jeff was being very non-committal. This gave him the cue to suggest walking back which we proceeded to do.

Most of the other swimmers were staying at the hotel, but past experience with Amy had shown this wasn't a good idea. None of them went to bed and they seemed to be hyperactive before races. They usually spent most of the night running about, and we knew in the case of Amy she would be like a wet rag the next day if she was with them, and totally incapable of swimming well.

We had been allotted a space in the camping field, which was only round the corner from the swimming-pool, so Jeff moved the camper round there. Amy and Paul were both excited about sleeping in the camper, so after they were in their bunk beds, we sat, with the TV turned down very low, waiting for them to go to sleep. I was praying that Paul would not get wheezy that night, and fate was kind. He slept right through, so did Amy. She was tired. It had been a long day and we had spent three hours travelling as well. We discussed her chances of making the final in her individual race. Terry had coached her and was very proud of her style of breaststroke. "I'm going to buy her that costume we saw, but don't tell her." Jeff was grinning.

I retorted, laughing, "She's crafty! She knows how to get round you."

There was a special bond between them. I wasn't jealous, but I wondered whether she turned to her dad more because I was always busy caring for Paul.

We went to bed, both finding it difficult to sleep, but nevertheless secure in the knowledge that the children were asleep.

Chapter Twenty-two

Jeff got up early to take Amy training and they walked round to the pool. I sat there making the most of the peace, savouring my cup of tea. Paul was still asleep, not surprising really. He had lain awake until midnight, giggling with delight to himself, obviously enjoying his new surroundings. He probably considered it fun to sleep in a bunk bed inside a camper.

As Amy's individual race was at nine o'clock I was hoping that he would sleep until then, so that I could pop in and watch it. No harm could come to him inside the van. I sat for a while with the radio on, listening to the news and weather. Then at eight-thirty Jeff came back. He had left Amy doing a warm up swim, and had come back to move the van into the car park, already full of cars at this early time, but there was an ideal spot under a tree for us.

"Good, he's still blotto! Let's have a quick coffee. We've got another twenty minutes."

I didn't think I could sit and drink coffee at such an exciting and nerve-racking time, but I put the kettle on the little gas ring and made some for Jeff.

"Come on, you as well, Carrie!"

I had a small cupful to keep him happy. I really had too much on my mind to relax. After we had finished our coffee there was still five minutes to go. I told Jeff to go on ahead. I was going to follow, but I didn't want to leave Paul for long in case he coughed or something and became wheezy.

I looked at my watch, one minute to go. I couldn't get much closer! I quietly opened the door of the camper and as I glanced back I saw that he was beginning to wake up. Oh no! I suddenly felt resentful. Surely five minutes to myself wasn't too much to expect. I did so want to see this race! I turned swiftly, handing Paul a glass of orange from the table and a biscuit. I handed him his box of cars that he loved so much, but already I was feeling torn both ways and full of guilt. "Here's a drink and biscuit, Paul. I'm only going to be five minutes. Stay in bed!"

He blinked sleepily at me. I knew he would obey me. He never got out of bed until he was told, but I just felt bad, going off and leaving him as he woke up.

I just about reached the pool in time to see Amy on the starting blocks. I hoped that she knew that I was there, but I didn't want to wave and distract her. Jeff was leaning over the rail, urging her to go faster as she swam. She swam a good race, winning her heat easily. It wasn't fast enough to get her in the final, but it earnt her a new personal best, which is every swimmer's goal. We knew she had years of good swimming ahead of her yet, and this was a very pleasing result. As she finished swimming her race my thoughts flew back to Paul. I had told him to stay in bed. He might have wanted the toilet! He hadn't been since last night, he would be feeling uncomfortable. I ran quickly back to the camper and opened the door cautiously. I needn't have worried. He was sitting up in bed holding two of his cars, the orange and biscuit had been consumed, and he greeted me with his heartwarming smile that I found so precious. I kissed his forehead and he wrinkled his nose, but he still beamed happily.

"Sorry to leave you, Paul. Do you want the toilet?"

He gave me his Makaton sign, and confirmed it by a firm shake of his head. Amazing! I thought, no way could I go that long. The chances are he would not go now until after breakfast.

I then proceeded to make him a breakfast of Weetabix and milk, and this was followed by toast and a cup of tea. If I was honest with myself, the main reason that Paul's face was wreathed in smiles when I came back was because he knew he would soon get his breakfast. Still, it didn't matter if he associated me with food. It was nice just to get a response. After about half an hour Jeff returned, armed

112

with a programme and all the times of the swimmers in Amy's age group written down.

"Where were you? She didn't make the final, but she did a PB!" he said proudly.

"I *was* there. I saw her just as she started, but I got held up because Paul woke up as I was coming out of the camper. I had to stop and give him a drink and talk to him."

"You should have left him. He would have been all right for five minutes."

I didn't pursue it, but I couldn't help thinking that it was all very well for Jeff to say that. There was no way that I could have just ignored him when he woke up. Paul wouldn't know where I'd gone or how long I was going to be if I didn't tell him. It was hard enough for him not being able to speak, but it would be even worse if I didn't communicate with him!

Paul had finished eating by now and I brought over a bowl of warm water for him to wash with. I reminded him again about the toilet and he suddenly pushed back his quilt, and with his usual clumsy gait, slid out of his bunk, making his way to the door housing the porta potti, the campers' independence from public toilets. When he had finished I went to help him as it flushed by pulling a knob, unlike our one at home. Paul had a fascination for toilets, which had to be kept at bay. If left to his own devices he would sit happily all day flushing it, revelling in the feeling of the water tingling the back of his legs. I brought him out and helped him to wash and clean his teeth. This was another chore he obviously felt was superfluous, so he needed encouragement. He then dressed himself with help. This all took a while, but it had been part of my daily life for such a long time that I accepted it as normal. Sometimes Paul would have fads about not wearing a particular tee-shirt or jumper, so I had brought a choice of three today. He chose an orange tee-shirt which did nothing to complement his navy cotton trousers. (He had to wear cotton because of his eczema.) However, I let him put that on. He had disregarded his new navy and white striped one, bought especially to match his trousers.

Amy was swimming in the relay later in the afternoon, but I hadn't yet worked out how I would see that. Jeff had.

"You can go on ahead of me this time. I will make sure he's OK before I join you."

I wasn't sure, but I didn't want to dampen the happy atmosphere. "Suppose that he isn't OK?"

"He will be. It's as safe as being in his bedroom. Carrie, you must stop being paranoid about him!"

His words were sensible, but the years of worry and uncertainty had taken their toll on me. It suddenly struck me that even with the help I had been given by the family, and the daily independence created by my job, I was not independent! Everything that I did without Paul relied on help provided by others. When things went wrong the ultimate responsibility lay with me, as his mother, and sometimes the weight of all this seemed just too much to bear.

"When is Amy coming back?" I enquired. "She must be hungry!"

"When she's had her swim down. I haven't told her yet, but after she's done the relay I thought we could walk round to the shopping centre and buy her that costume we saw."

In spite of his tough exterior Jeff was very susceptible to his daughter's cravings, and this was his way of showing her that he was proud of her achievement.

I smiled. "I'm going to tidy up a bit. Now that she's done one swim I'm going to get her to eat something before she does the next one."

Amy was not noted for her tidiness. She had left her quilt and nightie in a tangled heap on the floor, and as there wasn't much room to start off with I picked them up, more for our benefit than hers.

Jeff put on a country and western tape, and put the kettle on for yet another cup of tea. Paul sat, swaying to the music. He had always loved music and we knew this would keep him happy. I busied myself tidying things up and then I prepared lunch. Jeff and I had not had breakfast, and all we could get Amy to eat was one Weetabix with milk, but we had insisted on that before she got in the water.

I was doing salad, our little travelling fridge contained everything. Amy had been on a special diet for the last week, eating as much carbohydrates as possible to build up her energy. Since yesterday she was to have light foods whilst

114

competing, and salad with grilled quarter pounders was ideal. I opened a tin of new potatoes to put on the gas ring to complete the meal. Just then Amy appeared, accompanied by Diane, her long standing swimming friend, who was another swimmer in the relay team. She burst through the door. I jumped up, nervously.

"Calm down!" I knew I had to expect this when she was swimming.

"By the way, well done!"

"Mum! You didn't see my race!" she said accusingly.

"I did! But when I got there you were lining up. I didn't want to call to you."

"I thought maybe you were looking after Paul."

It hurt that she had assumed that I would have been too busy with Paul to come and watch her.

"Why couldn't Paul come and watch you?" enquired Diane. She had always liked Paul and she spent a lot of time at our house. He must have liked her because he allowed her to hug him.

"He can't watch me because he bites people and pushes them," said Amy, in such a matter of fact way, as if it was quite a usual thing to happen, although for her I suppose it was. Diane did not react with horror. She said, "People should be kind to him, shouldn't they, Paul?" She leaned over and kissed his cheek, and he rewarded her with a dazzling smile. It was brief, then his eyes moved towards me with the food.

I laughed. "You've just had your breakfast and now you want lunch?"

He nodded his head vigorously. Then as if to confirm it he opened the cupboard door and excitedly pulled out a plate. With clumsy movements he sat down at the table, quivering with anticipation and making sure that I did not forget him.

"OK, Paul. I get the message. Good boy! Diane are you staying for lunch?"

"No, thanks. Mum is taking me to McDonald's. See you at the warm up Amy. We're going to win, you know."

The determination in her voice was confirmed by the expression on both their faces. Hopefully, if Paul stayed in this good and happy mood, everything would be fine for me to watch her. We ate our lunch and found that Amy's hyper-tension was infectious. I knew how much it would mean to her to be part of the fastest relay team in Great Britain. We discussed the opposition. Leeds had a mean team of their own, with the advantage of swimming in their own home swimming-pool.

But Amy was feeling confident. "With Diane's 'fly and my breaststroke, coupled with Amelia doing freestyle and Kate doing backstroke, we'll take some beating!"

I looked at the set look on her face and marvelled at the killer instinct that winners are made of in one so young. Annette was exactly the same about her sport. It took first place over everything. There's no doubt that sports people are very special people, as well as their talent they have qualities of courage and dedication that us ordinary people lack.

Jeff regaled her with tips about her swimming. He knew what he was talking about as an ex-swimming instructor, but Amy was not taking in too much of this last minute advice.

"Dad! Are you coming back with me? It's warm-up time," she said, after he had finished.

"No. Mum is!" He looked at me pointedly. "I'll sort Paul out."

Paul was still in a happy mood. He had just had breakfast almost immediately followed by lunch, and life was good. I refrained from asking Jeff if Paul would be all right. I had recognised his look, and Paul seemed to be in such a good frame of mind.

There was an initial panic when Amy couldn't find her club costume and she was convinced that she had left it at home. I hadn't chanced that, without it she would not have been able to swim in the relay. I had tucked it under the seat with the spare towel and I got it out. I could see that she was getting really nervous now, so I took her over to the pool to give her a chance to warm up. I waved good-bye to Paul and Amy ruffled his hair.

"Dad will come, won't he?" she anxiously enquired.

"Of course! He wouldn't miss your race for anything!

116

Don't forget your costume, and good luck!" as she went to rush off.

I sat at the side of the pool, watching the swimmers warming up. This was the final day of the Nationals, and I was due at work tomorrow. I couldn't leave Paul at home now that Joe and Annette were working and out all day. He couldn't go to holiday playschool because there was no one to take and collect him, so bringing him with us had been the only thing to do. I interrupted my thoughts as I saw Jeff coming in and I waved to attract his attention.

"How was Paul when you left him?"

"OK, I left him a pot of Smarties and told him to eat them slowly."

I relaxed a bit more and then noticed that they were clearing the water and getting ready to start.

"Becley's in the third heat," said Jeff with eager anticipation. He had his stop watch and pen and paper handy, and it was impossible not to get caught up in the excitement of it all. The fastest eight teams would go through to the final and as we watched them swim he wrote down the times of the winning teams. By the time that Amy's heat had started we were on the edge of our seats, hearts pounding with excitement. Kate led off in the backstroke with a good start, and led the field, but in the changeover between her and Diane things went wrong. Diane took off late and they slipped back to third place. Now we watched with bated breath as Amy took over. It was a brilliant changeover, fast and effortless. She had pulled back half a metre on the second girl. This seemed to give her confidence and her stroke became more powerful as she motored through the water. Jeff was shouting, "Go! Go! Go!" and I was on my feet, too. Amelia took over from her and, with her long arms stretched in a rhythmic front crawl, she caught and overtook the second girl. There was a roar from the Becley supporters and she finished just behind the Leeds girl, in second place.

"They're in the final, seeded second fastest. If Kate and Diane can get their changeover right they'll win the gold medal!"

Chapter Twenty-three

The finals were in about half an hour, so we returned to the camper to have another cup of tea, leaving Amy with her coach, Terry. He was berating Kate and Diane about their changeover. It was a tense time for everyone. One silly mistake could cost them a gold medal. Looking at their faces, listening to him with concentration mapped all over them, it was hard to believe they were only at the tender age of eleven.

In the camper Paul was sitting under his quilt. Jeff had thought it safer to put him to bed, and his fingers were covered with the dye from the Smarties. Needless to say the pot was empty. I didn't grumble about the dye on the quilt cover. It was washable and it had kept him happy. I washed his hands and gave him a biscuit whilst we drank our tea. I remarked, "Jeff, he's been in the camper all day!"

"I know, after the gala finishes we'll go back to the shopping mall. Paul can have an ice-cream when I buy Amy's costume."

That made me feel a little less guilty, so we left him once more to go back for the final. We had left a tape on for him to listen to, and I knew that he wouldn't really miss us. Paul has always been content with his own company.

Jeff and I stood by the rail, no longer able to sit in our seats, whilst the teams lined up. Amy did not smile, her look was grim, but determination was etched all over her face.

"On your marks, set," — bang! went the gun and they were off. Once again Kate had a good start and was leading the field at the turn, Diane had a much better changeover, but the Leeds 'fly swimmer was more powerful, and stroked her way past Diane. As it came up to the changeover to Amy for the breaststroke she was lying second, with the girl from the Scottish team right on Kate's elbow, vying for second place.

"Go, Amy!" yelled Jeff.

I'm sure that with all the noise and the slap of the water against her swimming hat she could not hear him, but it made him feel better. I was yelling too. "Move! Kick those legs!"

Her dive was long, and she got into the rhythm of her stroke quickly and effortlessly. Inch by inch she was pulling away from the threat of the Scottish invasion, and as we watched she was gaining on the less powerful breaststroker from the Leeds team. She finished fractionally ahead of her, and Amelia dived in lying in first place. Amy had done her bit and all we could do now was watch. Although not the fastest over one hundred metres Amelia was an excellent sprint swimmer. She kept her lead, and although the Leeds girl fought her with hard determination, she stayed ahead and touched first. To the great delight of their band of supporters Becley had won a gold medal. They were the fastest medley relay team in Great Britain!

We were all in such an excited whirl afterwards. It was such a marvellous team effort. As they stood on the rostrum receiving their medals I felt so proud of Amy. As I looked at her face, shining with happiness, it somehow brought home to me Paul's handicaps even more. I asked myself again, fleetingly, why he had been born with everything against him. Amy was so lucky! The thought, brief though it was, tinged this happy moment with sadness.

The presentation ceremony was over and Amy rushed up, excitedly showing her medal.

"Well done love!" we both echoed, so proud of her. Jeff told her.

"We're going shopping when you've changed."

Amy laughed. She knew the routine, and had probably guessed what her treat would be. Jeff waited with a patience he didn't usually possess, but he was still basking in her glory!

I returned to the camper, and Paul.

"Mum's back, Paul. We're going for a walk soon before you turn into a recluse!"

He glared at me. There was a lazy streak in Paul and he found it more enjoyable listening to the tapes than the idea of going for a walk. I sat down with him. I guessed that Jeff would have to wait a little while for Amy. The girls team were on such a high, they were probably telling everyone in the changing room of their victory, if indeed there was anyone left that didn't know!

After about half an hour they appeared, Amy's face was still flushed with excitement.

"Come on folks! We have half an hour before the shops shut," remarked Jeff.

I looked dubiously at Paul, but I knew he should get some exercise. He won't show off with Jeff around, I thought to myself.

We left the camper. Amy had her hand in Jeff's and they relived the race yet again, discussing it through to the end of it. I walked behind with Paul. He was dragging his feet, but when Jeff turned around and urged us to hurry he suddenly thrust his arm through mine. He walked with uncertain steps, stumbling every so often. I could feel the tension within him, and as usual it transferred itself into me as well. We walked past a group of Becley supporters, who called out greetings to us, and we acknowledged them, but kept walking. I wasn't enjoying this, I just wanted to get it over and done with. Paul's reluctance was so obvious and he was scraping the toe of his left shoe along the ground. He had gone through so many toes of his shoes. It would mean another pair of shoes, and I would be left with one more perfectly good right shoe to go with the other eight.

Jeff and Amy were further ahead now, and I knew that Paul was not going to walk at a faster pace. Suddenly, like lightning, he moved! He gave a loud scream, as though in pain, and fiercely dragged my arm towards his mouth. I cannot say it was a complete surprise. I had been expecting something, but his strength when angry was far superior to mine. I screamed with pain when he sank his teeth into my arm and he jumped away, having adequately demonstrated his feelings about going for a walk with me! The next thing I saw was Jeff's angry face.

"No, Paul! How dare you bite your mother!"

Then a loud resounding slap as his hand met Paul's rear end. Paul gulped with shock. The slap had hurt him and he stood with his head bowed, doing his best to retreat into his own safe little world.

I felt dizzy with shock. Already my arm was swelling and the purple teeth marks could clearly be seen. He had never attacked me with such venom before and I couldn't seem to stop the tears from running down my face. I was weeping for Paul and myself, I think.

"It's not his fault, Jeff! I knew he didn't want to go out. He was tense!"

"Don't make excuses for him. He's going to learn that he can't just attack you when he feels like it!" And turning to Paul, he said, "Showing your paddy just because you don't want to go for a walk!"

I dried my eyes. Amy was looking at my arm. "Oh, Mum, I don't like that nasty bruise! Paul I don't like you when you hurt Mum."

"Don't blame him, Amy, when he can't speak! I will take him back to the camper and you and Dad can go and get your shopping."

But Jeff was not having this. "No, Paul *will* come for a walk!" He looked strong and commanding. "Amy, you walk with Mum, and Paul *you* are walking with me, and let's see if you want to try and take lumps out of me!"

Needless to say, the crisis passed. Paul was a model of good behaviour with Jeff, and we went and bought Amy's costume, but this incident had spoilt the day for me, and upset Amy. I felt nervous and unsettled, and even though we looked around the cathedral, and had tea in the tea room afterwards, my heart was not in it. I just wanted to get Paul back to familiar surroundings.

I realised that now, even more, my life was becoming split into two. Paul on one side, living life in his own way and at his own pace, and the family on the other. When we tried to fit Paul in with our pace of life it didn't work!

121

f

Chapter Twenty-four

I wore a long-sleeved blouse, although the weather was very
hot, to hide the teeth marks on my arm from prying eyes.
It had swollen up and ached continuously, so after a week
I went to the doctor. He raised his eyebrows with amazement.

"Why didn't you come before?"

"I thought that it would get better on its own."

The truth was I was too ashamed to let people know how
brutal Paul could be when he was angry. Since the last
occasion, although I dearly loved the other side of his nature,
I actually felt scared of being left with him. Amy was, too!
He didn't try it on Joe and Annette for some reason, but he
pushed and tried to bite Amy once or twice, although not
with quite the same aggressiveness that he had shown towards
me.

The doctor eyed me shrewdly. "I will give you some anti-
inflammatory pills and pain killers. It hasn't gone septic, but
I can see you had a nasty bite!"

"Yes, doctor. It had unnerved me. I'm getting too old
for shocks like that!" I laughed, was I sounding like Methu-
selah?

"Mrs Carter," he paused and became serious. "Do you
think that it's time to put Paul's name on a waiting list for
accommodation for when he's older? You will find as he
grows older that it's harder to cope with him."

Six months ago I would have scorned those words, and
told him we could cope as a family, but now I was realising
that it was no longer true. I wouldn't live forever. How could
I pass all of Paul's problems on to his brother and sisters.
They were entitled to a life of their own, too, and now I felt

122

they were beginning to suffer. I knew his idea was sensible and I nodded. My spirit felt defeated.

He handed me a piece of paper. "This is the address to write to, and then they will want to see you, and Paul."

I thanked him and took my leave, and my thoughts whirled all the way home.

My conscience was divided in half. On one side was Paul. I was trying to compensate to him for being handicapped by taking care of him myself. I felt to blame. After all he had grown inside my body, and I had given birth to him. I had wanted to provide him with the love and care of a family life for ever.

On the other side of my conscience there were Jeff and the family. I never seemed to have much time for them. I had to miss out on doing a lot of things with them. Joe and Annette had suffered more than Amy because I'd had precious little time to spend with them and share social times. I had a growing feeling that although no one voiced it, there was resentment towards Paul creeping in.

Oh God! Which way could I turn? Whatever I did would hurt someone! When I got home I told Jeff of my decision and asked him how he felt about it.

"I think it's a wise decision, but it had to come from you."

I knew what he meant. Jeff was a stepfather, and he wanted me to feel that he had not influenced me to do this. I still marvelled at the fact that he had always been prepared to share the problems with me.

About a week after I had written to them, the local Mencap Society sent a representative to see Paul. She filled in forms and wrote notes, and then when she had finished she told me, "There's such a long waiting list, and because of the government cut-backs accommodation is so limited that Paul wouldn't even be considered until he's nineteen, unless, of course, you really can't cope."

I found myself saying, "It's getting a lot harder now. I have a large family."

She looked down at her notes. "Not strong enough, I'm afraid! You're able to hold a full-time job down, and two of your children are adults and able to help more now."

I looked at her in dismay. Never mind the stress involved,

fighting to hold the job down! The uncertainties of Paul's moods, his illnesses, epileptic fits, wheezing and now aggression too! It wasn't to our credit that we had coped and done our best. It was against us! Didn't she realise that I was not twenty-five any more! I was forty-three, and had had a hard life one way or another. As if reading my thoughts she said, "Of course, as he gets older, and you do, things will become harder, but rest assured that if anything happens to you or your husband Paul will be taken care of."

She then stood up and said good-bye to Paul, who had decided in this instant to be a model of good behaviour!

"What a nice looking boy, what a shame." Ruffling his hair as she passed him, and he treated her to a dazzling smile.

After she had gone I felt a mixture of relief and hopelessness. I didn't have to make a decision yet, but deep down I wanted to.

The school holidays passed without any major happenings, and then Paul and Amy returned to school to commence the autumn term. Amy was now going to a school near to the swimming club, and as she was training every night of the week, she would go there straight from school, and Jeff or I would pick her up afterwards. Then Joe graduated from a scooter to a car. When he passed his test be borrowed my car to go and pick her up. This made life easier for me. All I had to do was to cook the dinner and get Paul off to bed. He was always tired after a day at school, and went between seven and eight o'clock. He has never had the same physical stamina as the others.

I still had my home help baby-sitter. Marie was good and reliable. She also did ironing for me, and I'm glad to say that Paul had never given her any trouble. We paid quite highly for this service, but for the peace of mind it gave me it was well worth it.

Annette had written off to find out about summer camps in America, which involved sports coaching of children on holiday. She was running really well and had earnt herself many medals and trophies. She felt there were more opportunities in the States, and consequently June 1987 found her flying to New York State to further her ambition. We were a little concerned because she had thrown up a good job in the bank, but she had to get this itch out of her system. She had gone through the usual adolescent problems of stubbornness and quarrelsome attitudes, but this had all been resolved now and we parted warmly, and needless to say, I missed her.

Paul was now sixteen, and his health took a downward plunge again. His asthma worsened and even his nebuliser didn't seem to help him any more. I felt desperate! I thought he was dying, and felt ashamed of myself for wanting to have him taken into care previously. He spent the six weeks from September 1987 until mid-October in and out of hospital. As soon as he was put on the hospital nebuliser his breathing stabilised. Then he was sent home the next day, but within twenty-four hours he was back in again. I lost several nights of sleep when he had been bad in the small hours of the morning and had to be taken to hospital. Getting up to go to work and carry on normally was very difficult. I spent every lunch-time at the hospital with him, so that I could be near when he was ill. I was in despair! I didn't know what I was doing wrong, or not doing right as the case might be. After his last attack, which was the worst, they decided to keep him in for two days. I arrived after work to see him, and as I reached the end of the children's ward where his bed was situated, a wave of panic passed through me when I saw that it was empty. None of the children were in their beds, they were all up, either in the TV room, or sitting at the table, eating. Silly me! He's having supper, I thought.

A nurse came hurrying up to me, overworked and underpaid no doubt, judging by her attitude.

"You will find Paul in a room on his own," she said curtly. "First he bit another child and then he bit sister!" There was a note of grudging admiration as she finished her sentence, as if only Paul had dared to stand up to such an imposing figure. I felt shocked and embarrassed by his behaviour, but instinctively stood up for him.

"He hasn't been well! This is his fifth time in hospital in six weeks!"

She cut in, "Well there's nothing wrong with him now, and when he threw his cars at sister I had to duck too, or I would have received a lorry full in the face!"

By now we had reached the door to his room. There was a glass partition, and I could see Paul through it. He lay miserably on his bed. He had no toys, not even soft ones, to play with, and it was almost like being in prison. On the side was an empty tray with plastic plates and a cup. I hadn't used plastic for him at home for years! I went in warily, but he gave me a dazzling smile and I put my arms around him. "Well, my son," I asked, "what have you been up to now?"

Chapter Twenty-five

It's funny, no matter how much your children upset you at times, when someone else is annoyed with them, how you almost feel that they're being misjudged. Of course it was very wrong for Paul to bite people, particularly another child who was ill, but it was a cruel trick that nature had played on him. He couldn't speak! Wouldn't it have been easier and more comforting for him, over the years, to be able to say, "I don't feel well. Please help me!"

Could any of us imagine the horror of being trapped in your own lonely world, able to understand what is said to you, but totally unable to convey your side of things.

All this was flowing through my mind as I looked at the pathetic little figure, and I wondered again why fate had been so cruel to him. As I sat there the door was pushed open and sister stood there. I, too, marvelled at his audacity in biting her. She would have made two of Paul. She was big upwards and outwards, and had an imposing voice to match.

"Mrs Carter, Paul behaved like a little monster!"

"Yes, I'm sorry," I said miserably.

She went on without giving me a chance to speak further.

"He bit a little boy in the next bed whilst he was eating a bar of chocolate and then when I told him off he threw his cars at me, I took them off him because it was dangerous to have them flying around, and then he bit me, too!"

She flourished her large arm, well covered in flesh, in front of me, and I remember thinking she had been luckier than me, his teeth had only faintly marked the skin, probably due to her superfluous padding. She went on: "He can't stay here any longer. No one can cope with him! He needs constant supervision all day long, and my staff haven't got the time, and they are all scared of him."

I became bolder. "But he's ill. I can't keep his breathing stable at home!" Fear struck me again. I didn't want to lose him.

At that moment there was a tap at the door and the house doctor came in. "Hello Paul, Hello Mum. Sister, Mrs Jones wants to talk to you about her son's medication."

"OK, doctor." Sister's attitude changed to one of compliancy, and to my great relief she hurried off to see Mrs Jones.

The doctor was kindly and understanding. He did not refer to Paul's misdemeanours in any way. He checked his chest and seemed satisfied that it was better, but I was anxious.

"I don't understand why he has to keep coming in. I just can't keep his breathing stable at home."

"Mm," he said, thoughtfully. "I see we've gone through the usual allergies, dogs, dust, trees, pollen. All or one of these contribute, but basically they can all be eliminated, and it can still be something else causing it that we never even thought of."

"So what is the answer?" I was puzzled.

"Prevention is better than cure. Instead of only nebulising him when he's ill, if it's done twice a day, morning and evening, it may stop him from being ill so often."

I tried to accept this but it didn't stop the thoughts from going through my mind. The nebulising process took nearly an hour. That would mean I would have to wake him up at six o'clock every day to have it. Then it would take another hour to wash him, supervise his dressing and give him his breakfast in readiness for school. Then, if there was any time left, I would have to get ready for work. Luckily Amy was independent enough to sort herself out now. I suppose this all sounded very selfish of me, but wasn't there another way?

"But, doctor, I thought I was told that Paul was not to get too dependent on his nebuliser!"

He looked at me sympathetically, realising he had given me yet another chore to do. "He needs the Ventolin to keep his air passages open so that he can breathe properly. His chest is not in a good state."

"I see." I didn't like the sound of this. I knew I must stop feeling sorry for myself and get on and help Paul.

So I took him home, armed with a bag full of medication: three sorts of medicine to take. I felt so sad to think that a boy so young needed all these things to keep him alive. I had found the boy that Paul had bitten. His bite, I'm glad to say, was not a bad one, but I had insisted that Paul was to shake hands with him as a gesture of apology for what he had done. I bought him some more chocolate and explained that Paul's aggression was caused because he wanted some chocolate but couldn't speak to ask for it. The lad understood more than his mother did and I was touched by his kindness when he bought a Matchbox car for Paul, and gave it to him when we left the ward. Everyone else was glad to see us go. Paul was considered to be some sort of monster. Sister sniffed as we walked past, which only made it more apparent that this thirteen-year-old boy was far more mature for his years than any of those adults were!

A couple of days after we arrived home it was the half term week, so I decided to finish up my last week of holiday left from work and to spend some time taking Paul and Amy out. This particular morning, after Jeff and Joe had gone to work, I took Paul his breakfast in bed. He sat up expectantly. I was learning to cope with nebulising, and his breathing was more stable. I put the tray of porridge and a cup of tea on his lap, and he quivered excitedly.

"Calm down, Paul. You'll spill it!" I admonished him lightly.

"When you've eaten that I'm going to take you and Amy out in the car." I added, "We may even have lunch out later."

He smiled his approval, and I left him eating whilst I made sure that Amy was getting up. She was pleased at the thought of having lunch out and was trying to decide what to wear.

"Mum, are you wearing a dress or trousers?"

She was at an age where she liked to copy me. "A skirt and jumper, I think. The wind is a bit cold today."

Suddenly I heard a noise as if someone was choking, followed by a high-pitched scream. It was Paul! I raced in to his bedroom. He was in his bed, bent over, and his breakfast tray fell with a crash to the floor. As my frightened eyes took in the scene I could see he was suffering an epileptic fit. This was the first one I had witnessed on my own, without Jeff to help me. I tried not to panic and remember all I had been told, not to put my hand in his mouth because he could bite it off in this semi-conscious state. I couldn't help the fear and very deep compassion from churning through the very depths of my being for this son of mine!

An epileptic fit is distressing to watch, the twitching spasms of the limbs, the rolling of the eyes making the whites become apparent. He had fallen slumped forward and I turned his head, praying he would not swallow his tongue. The choking noises continued and I asked God yet again not to let him die!

All this probably lasted about two minutes, but it seemed interminable to me and my mental agony continued until I saw his eyes flicker open. I felt relief flooding through me.

"Oh, Paul!" Although a little pale, he seemed OK. "You did frighten me. Are you OK, son?"

He nodded assent, according to the doctor he probably didn't remember anything. However, the initial scream was for help because he knew that something was wrong. My heart ached for him. Amy disturbed my thoughts. "Oh, he's had a fit. So now we can't go out!"

"Amy, don't be so selfish! You know he's unlikely to have another one for about three months as he's just had one. We'll let him rest and go out a bit later but I promise we'll have lunch out!"

She was becoming hard and selfish, only thinking of herself, I thought, but my conscience told me that this was the result of years of happenings and uncertainty. I tucked Paul's quilt around him and left the room.

"How tidy is your room, Amy?"

"OK, I'll tidy it. I get the message!"

Amy's room was a standing joke. Jeff said she could reach her bunk bed without a ladder simply by standing on top of all the clothes she left on the floor.

I thought I heard a choking noise again. Really my nerves were getting so bad. But then I heard it again and I couldn't believe it!

I rushed into Paul's room again to witness another fit,

just as distressing as the last. I gulped, and went through the proper motions again, trying desperately to keep myself together. But cruel fate had not finished with Paul yet! Within ten minutes he had suffered three fits, and Amy was, by now, hysterical. I telephoned 999 because I didn't really know what else to do. Paul had never had more than one fit on any one occasion before, and they had always been spaced at several months apart.

When I told the emergency services what had happened they sent an ambulance. Amy was very shaken up by what had happened, and I didn't want to leave her on her own. She was, after all, only twelve years old, so I telephoned Jeff at work, and he said he would meet me at the hospital to take her home with him. When the ambulance arrived Paul was sleeping, but by now I was expecting him to have fits all the time because my nerves were shattered.

The ambulance men were very caring. They gave him oxygen as a precaution and I sat by the still little figure with the mask over his face, wondering if this nightmare would ever end. Amy was silent, and after seeing her pale face, one of the men joked with her, "Jim and I didn't know we'd be giving a ride to such an important young lady!"

He had spotted her medals and trophies lined up on the shelf. It was amazing how observant these ambulance men were and how cheerful in the midst of such a stressful job. I tried to console myself that Paul wasn't desperately ill. The ambulance drove at moderate speed without the blue light flashing, and Amy brightened up and started telling them about some of her most notable swims. We arrived at the hospital without further incident, but Paul was not taken to the children's ward. He was taken to casualty. After we had been there for a few minutes and Paul's oxygen mask had been removed, to my intense relief I noticed his colour returning. He had been put in a bed with bars at the side, no doubt in case he had another fit and fell out of bed.

A nurse had gone through the usual written preliminaries, and then Jeff arrived. He had rushed from work and I was relieved that he could take Amy home to a more comforting environment. I said to him, "Bye, love. I'll get home when I can," and aside to Amy, "Sorry I let you down today."

I suddenly remembered that we had been going out for lunch. Amy hugged me.

"I do love you, Mum, and Paul, will he be all right?"

"Of course!" I laughed with a confidence that I didn't feel.

Jeff quietly looked at Paul and then turned to me. "Ring me when you've finished here and Paul is settled. I'll bring the car to collect you."

He kissed me gently and they went. I remember Amy's pale face with red-rimmed eyes looking at me, and it haunted me!

Chapter Twenty-six

I pulled up my chair close to the bed and watched the doctor examining Paul. When he had finished he put down his stethoscope and said, "I believe the fits are the onset of an infection. Paul has a temperature and a sore throat. Did he vomit?"

"No, doctor. He made a choking noise but he didn't vomit."

"We will keep him in for a few days for observation. I'm sure that you must need a break at home."

"Thank you, doctor. Those fits really did frighten me."

So once again we were reprieved. Maybe lying there looking so helpless, so totally dependent on others made Paul's condition appear worse in my eyes. I didn't mean to be an alarmist. I had always tried to minimise his problems in the hope that they would lessen as he grew up. Oh that phrase, 'He'll grow out of it', was well used and abused I think. Paul was not put in the children's ward again. I think sister had put her foot down, ill or not, she did not have much time for him. He was put in the men's ward. Of course, chronologically he was sixteen, and maybe he would think twice about biting men, who were taller and stronger than himself. On the third day, having not had any more fits, he developed a cold. A cold! Surely, I thought, he won't have multiple fits every time he gets one! The doctor decided to talk to me that day about Paul, so I listened with my usual feelings of trepidation, anxious for what I might hear.

"Now that Paul's cold has come out we need to check that there wasn't another reason for three fits in succession."

"What sort of reason could there be?" I asked.

"Let's wait and see." Was all I was told. It was just as well that the doctors were not prepared to speculate and tell me possibilities.

The next day an ambulance came to take Paul to the brain hospital and I went with him. Jeff had taken some days off to be with Amy and I hoped he would take her out a bit. As far as I was concerned her holiday was spoilt, and my week was spent at the hospital! We spent a day at the brain hospital having Paul tested, and also a scan. I was not allowed in with him whilst he was being tested, but I was waiting by his bed for him when he returned. It didn't seem to have worried him. He was bright and happy, and the nurses here liked him. They were seeing the lovely side of his nature, which few people have ever been able to resist. At the end of the day the ambulance took us back to the local hospital, accompanied by a young nurse who Paul had obviously taken to. She was helping him to line his cars up on the seat.

"He's so bright, Mrs Carter. He knows everything that we say to him!"

"I've always thought that, too. It seems so unfair that he can't talk!"

I suppose it must seem strange to the reader calling a boy of sixteen who cannot read, write or speak, bright, but when Paul cared to leave his isolated inner world he could respond to words and commands effortlessly. Without speech, to know the difference between putting a car *over* or *under* a seat, I thought, was amazing.

I wiped his runny nose gently as he was too preoccupied to be concerned about such trivialities. We had arrived back at the hospital now and Paul, to his great delight, was put into a wheel-chair and taken back to the ward. "This is a treat, but it won't be a habit!" I told him laughingly, and explained to the ambulance men. "He can be a bit lazy about walking. It took him years to learn, so I want him to know that he can still do it!"

They laughed too, and Paul joined in, understanding absolutely what I had said. Today was his treat and he was getting his own way. The sister in this ward was much nicer than the one in the children's ward. She welcomed us back warmly and told me that the doctor would see me tomorrow with Paul's results. I looked at her face, which gave nothing away, and I knew I would just have to wait for the news, good or bad. I made sure that Paul was comfortable for the night, thanking the nurse who had accompanied us in the ambulance. I knew I must think about getting home. I had barely seen the family this week, only snatching a hurried breakfast before quickly doing my chores, and then on to the hospital every day. We did manage to have our evening meal together which, most days, Jeff had cooked. Once or twice I left a casserole slowly cooking and today was one of those days.

As I kissed Paul and took my leave I tried not to look at some of the elderly men lying there, obviously very ill. The atmosphere was depressing and I couldn't help thinking why my son, at only sixteen, was in and out of hospital with such regularity. It was a way of life for him now. Was he always going to be an invalid? That word conjured up a picture of someone always in bed. In Paul's case that was not true. He literally lived his life until he was too ill to stand up. In my eyes he was a hero! He had always fought his illnesses as much as he could.

As my car pulled into the drive I saw that the lights were on. It was only seven o'clock, but the evenings were drawing in. Of course, next week it would be November! I hadn't even started to think about Christmas. Soon we would be working the extra days at work.

I got out of the car, carefully locking the door. As I went in Jeff and Amy were sitting, he was in the armchair and she was perched on the arm of it, laughing at some silly comedy programme. They looked so close I felt a pang of disappointment for something I was missing out on. Jeff turned as he heard the front door close.

"Mum's here! Hi love, I'll dish up dinner in a minute. How's Paul?"

I kissed them both. "He's coming home tomorrow."

Amy laughed. "Just in time to go back to school. He didn't do that very well!"

We sat down to dinner. I wasn't really hungry. My mind was wandering on, thinking about what I might be told tomorrow, but I made an effort to eat a little. Jeff knew what was on my mind but he refrained from mentioning

135

it whilst Amy was around.

"Did you tell Mum about your swim?"

Oh God! I had forgotten! I guiltily switched my thoughts back to Amy. "I was going to ask you how it went this afternoon, Amy." I had remembered that she was swimming for Kent in the breaststroke against six other county champions, including her great rival, the girl from Essex.

"I won! and I broke the record!"

"Well done darling. I'm proud of you!" And so I was. "I'll come and watch you again soon. Things will get better."

She made no comment. I wanted her to believe me and I wanted to believe myself.

After we had finished our meal I cleared away the dishes and stacked them in the dish washer. Amy suddenly remembered some homework she had to do before returning to school. This was typical of her. She was never organised and, as she wanted to go and see Diane tomorrow, she only had this evening left to do it. She shut herself in her room, supposedly to concentrate on her essay, but I could hear her TV on. We had bought her that as a present but had frequently regretted it as a rash decision.

"I'm sorry I haven't seen much of you this week. I'm bringing Paul home tomorrow after I get his results and then we'll get back to normal." I told Jeff.

"Yes." Jeff sighed. He must have been thinking like me, what is normal? Is our life normal? Only normal for us I suppose. Did he ever think he had bitten off more than he could chew? It was just as well that we had a daughter of our own but I didn't like to think that was the reason he stayed with me. I felt the urge to voice my thoughts.

"Do you sometimes feel my problems are too much for you to bear?" I waited, wondering what he would say. He was thoughtful, not answering immediately.

"I can bear them, but can you? You seem to be so tied up all the time."

I did not answer. I could not. I knew it was true but I couldn't see how anything could change. We sat, the TV was on, but I couldn't take in any of it. Eventually I excused myself to go to bed. Tomorrow was another day. Jeff kissed me goodnight. "Don't worry about the results. He'll be OK."

136

I went to bed wondering whether he really believed that. I wasn't sure I did.

The next day, which was Sunday, I was up early. I hadn't slept that well so I tidied up and put some washing in the machine. Amy and Joe were still asleep, but Jeff got up and we ate our porridge together.

"Do you want me to come and collect him with you?"

I did really because I was frightened of what I might be told, but I knew that he had a job to do on his car that was of paramount importance. He needed it for work on Monday.

"No, that's OK. I won't be that long. I'll put the chicken in the oven, if you can get Joe to do the veg for lunch."

I kissed Jeff and set off with the all too familiar feelings running amok inside me. When I arrived at the hospital it was mid-morning, and tea and coffee were being served. Paul was sitting in a chair next to his bed, clutching his favourite little red sports car in his hand. I knew he had slept well because I had telephoned at eight o'clock and he looked reasonably relaxed and happy. I was treated to a bright smile and he allowed me to kiss his cheek.

The smiling nurse, Jenny, who had accompanied us to the brain hospital, came past, stopping briefly to talk to us. "Well, Paul, you certainly love your tum! He's had Weetabix, yoghurt and baked beans on toast for breakfast, and loads of orange juice!"

"Yes, he does eat well." We all smiled including Paul who loved the mention of food.

She moved on and I sat with Paul, waiting for the doctor to come and see us. He was already going round the ward. He was now two beds away, accompanied by sister. I tried to keep bright. "We've got chicken at home for dinner, Paul, your favourite!" I realised my words were a mistake as soon as I'd said them. Paul gave a loud whoop of glee and jumped out of the chair. He dragged out the holdall from under the bed and proceeded to put everything from the locker into it.

"We're not going yet, Paul!" Oh dear, I didn't want a scene. How would he take that? He continued to put everything into the holdall, doing his best to fold his creased pyjamas in the same way as I did. The doctor was only one bed away now, I willed him to hurry. Paul stopped and handed me his bottle of orange squash. He wasn't leaving it behind! "Do you want a drink?"

That distracted him momentarily, and before I could stop him he had headed off to the kitchen. I followed slowly, in time to see him returning with a clean plastic mug and a jug with a lid containing water, graciously provided by a student nurse. I guided his hand whilst he poured in the orange and added the water. He downed it in three gulps. He was always very enthusiastic about drinking.

By now the doctor had finished at the next bed. The curtains were pulled back and he made his way towards us. Sister came with him.

"Hello, Paul. Let's make sure you're fit and well."

Paul, good-humouredly allowed his chest to be examined.

"I see your bag is already packed," he smiled. "Yes, you can take him home. His cold has not gone to his chest."

He rustled the papers in his hand. "The brain scan shows there is definitely no brain tumour or abnormal cells. We cannot explain why there was an increase in fits, but I'm glad to say there is no ominous reason for it."

"Oh wonderful!" I felt as if I had just passed a very difficult exam. He went on, "However we are going to give Paul anti-convulsant drugs. I realise he is now on a lot of medication, but he will have a blood test every six months to make sure all is OK."

"Will it stop the fits completely, doctor?"

"For most of the time, yes. He will go back to having one occasionally."

"That is a relief. I hate to see him like that!"

"The thing you must be aware of is that this medication can cause more aggression, and also increase hyperactivity."

I shrugged. This was not good news but what other choice was there? So, armed with a paper bag full of medication, once again Paul and I went home.

Chapter Twenty-seven

The doctor had not exaggerated about the effects of the medication. I can only describe the next month as a living hell!

My day started at six o'clock. Nebulising Paul took an hour. Then I got him up for breakfast and he dressed afterwards. However, once down in the kitchen I found I could not leave him for a moment to answer the door or the telephone. I would come back to find, not only had he eaten all his breakfast, stuffing it down like some wild animal, but he had turned into a one man destruction team on the rampage! The contents of the fridge were turned out onto the floor, with anything edible consumed. He drank down a complete two litre bottle of undiluted orange squash one morning and promptly vomited it all back again. Another time he had used six slices of bread and half a pound of margarine to make a sandwich, and when I took it off him, saying he would be sick, he flew at me in a rage like a person possessed! I managed to dodge the bite, so in extreme frustration he bit himself on the wrist until he bled, which I found just as upsetting. I could not reason with him. He was hyperactive and aggressive, and as I was alone in the house at the time it was quite frightening. Evidently this behaviour was reserved exclusively for me, as Marie, our home help, had no complaints. No one could realise just what hell I was going through!

After a week of it I decided to give him his breakfast in bed and try to keep him in his bedroom until the coach arrived to collect him. This worked up to a point, but he was cute enough that when the coach tooted and I accompanied him downstairs and turned to open the front door, he would

move like lightning, and grab the nearest edible object. One
morning he triumphantly presented himself at the coach door
with a bowl of cold potatoes and baked beans, much to the
annoyance of the coach escort.

"No food allowed on the coach, Paul. It might upset the
others!"

"I don't advise you to take it off him. He's not to be
reasoned with!" I warned her. She looked at Paul's set face
and decided against it, but a couple of days later I received
a letter of complaint, pointing out that I was breaking the
coach company's rules and regulations.

All this was happening before eight o'clock in the morning,
and then I had to go to work and carry on normally. It's not
something you could ever expect someone who hasn't suffered
it to understand.

I knew Paul had got the upper hand. He recognised that as
a woman I was not physically strong enough to stop him. In
a temper his strength became formidable. Part of my problem
was that I knew why he was like this, and it grieved me so
much because it was not his fault that I could not bear to
physically slap him or hurt him in retaliation. There was still
the feeling that if I wasn't his mother maybe he would not
have had all these problems. He may not have even been
handicapped!

All the while that I was with Paul now I could not leave
him, not even to go to the toilet. He was destructive and a
danger to himself, too. It was like being in prison and I knew
I would have to talk to someone and get help. I went to talk
to our family doctor after discussing it with Jeff. I was not
offered tranquillisers and I did not want them. He arranged
for a social worker to call and she came on my day off
whilst Paul was at school.

Mrs Friston was such a nice lady, to this day I have much
to thank her for. She listened to my problems, made notes,
and then asked me questions. Finally, she said, "You certainly
have had a life of worry, my dear! I wonder you feel sane!"

I gulped. "I came close to a nervous breakdown several
years ago but luckily I managed to get over it, but Paul is
worse now than he ever was then."

"This is often what happens. The problem grows with

140

the child and it causes a gulf in the family. I see your husband is Paul's stepfather. What has he said about all this?"

The word 'stepfather' grated on me. I frequently felt guilty for all the stress I had piled on to him during our years together. Mark only saw Paul occasionally now that the others were grown up and only Joe was at home.

"He leaves decisions about Paul to me. He doesn't want me to feel that he pressures me over Paul, but I'm sure he must be fed up. We can't do much together, only when Paul goes to the Cedars once a month for respite care."

She was busily writing in her book.

"Well, I'm going to make an appointment for you and Paul to go and see a child psychologist, and I will recommend that residential care should be made available for him. Unfortunately, unless you fall apart or die, it doesn't usually happen. Sorry to be so blunt but that is the situation."

I laughed. "Well, let's hope that won't happen!"

It was no good being bitter. I knew exactly what she meant. As she got up to leave she turned and told me in a confidential tone.

"We at social services have a very guilty conscience about you, Mrs Carter. Somehow the system has missed you out. From the moment Paul's handicap was diagnosed it was your right to have a social worker to help you and give you moral support. Until your doctor contacted me no one knew you were without one. How have you managed all these years?"

"With the support and help from a wonderful family," I replied warmly, and my heart felt a feeling of gratitude course through it for all the patience and understanding they had shown Paul and myself. I must have seemed quite remote to them at times.

Two weeks after my visit from Mrs Friston I received a letter from Dr Bass, the psychologist, and an appointment had been made for me to attend her clinic. I was told that there was no need to bring Paul. Dr Bass regularly visited him at school and knew him well, as I was to find out. When I arrived at the centre, which was a brand new building, I sat in the reception area until a buzzer sounded. The receptionist pointed the way to Dr Bass's office and I walked through, not knowing quite what to expect.

She was seated at her desk as I entered, and she rose to shake hands with me. I was surprised at her appearance, small and slight, with her hair cut short. My mind had created the image of a tall matronly person with grey hair in a bun, wearing a pince-nez.

"How do you do, Mrs Carter. I am Dr Bass."

I shook hands. "How do you do?"

"Well to get straight to the point about your lovable little monster."

I smiled. "That just about sums him up!"

I soon realised that her fragile appearance belied her nature. She was tough, assertive and straight to the point without mincing her words.

"I actually heard about Paul before I met him on a professional level. I have a daughter, Sarah, with Down's syndrome, and Paul met up with her at holiday playschool." She laughed. "She showed me the bite when she came home!"

"My God! How could he let me down like that." I said involuntarily. I was filled with horror. "I am so sorry. I never knew!"

But Dr Bass was finding it very amusing.

"Don't worry! Sarah has finally met her match at last! She's a little devil and pulls everyone's hair. Paul decided he wasn't having it and retaliated."

"I see!" What a sensible woman she was, I was thinking. She must have been tempted to defend her daughter, but she was fair minded and prepared to see things from another point of view. As I listened to her I marvelled that she had managed to pursue such a specialised career. She must have a degree in child psychology. How had she found the time?

"Tell me about a typical day in your life with Paul."

Now that I was talking to someone with a similar problem it was even easier to discuss it. I found myself pouring out everything; his aggression, destructiveness, my inability to leave him even for a minute unattended, my feelings of despair, weariness, depression and total inability to cope. The effect it was having on us as a family, my guilt, which I found hard to bear, and my feelings of failure. My worry that he would die when he became ill, and when I had finished I covered my face with my hands and sobbed.

142

All the years of pent-up emotions and fears had been released and I had, at last, put my innermost thoughts into words.

She left me to pull myself together without making comment. We were twin souls and sympathy was not the answer. I heard her ordering coffee over her intercom, and by the time it was brought in I had myself under control again. I asked her. "How can you cope with your life so well, and pursue this career as well?"

She smiled. "We all appear OK on the surface until some-one digs deeper. But I get lots of help. I always have done. My mother is marvellous. My husband gets a good salary. He is a consultant surgeon, and we have a nanny, always have done, for Sarah. With all this help I'm able to have lots of time off, and don't forget, I only have one child."

I felt as if I had known this lady for years. She was honest and practical. She went on.

"Why do you think you are frightened when Paul is ill?"

I gulped. "I'm terrified that he's going to die!"

"There is always a risk that an asthma attack can carry him off but it's not your fault."

So my fears were not irrational! Someone had voiced my thoughts and somehow it made the knowledge easier to bear. At that time I began to come to terms with the future in my mind.

"I don't know if I can find a place for Paul at the Cedars. They are so short of staff and it will be closing in the next two years because the residents are being moved into smaller bungalows, more like family units.

I had been to the meeting and knew about this. It was no surprise. "I would be prepared to have him at home at the weekend. Just to have the early morning to myself to quietly get ready for work would be heaven!"

"Well, I don't make any promises, I will try, but I think you will have to wait until he's nineteen."

This was really what I had expected but just talking had helped. I thanked her and prepared to go. As I reached the door and we shook hands again she added, "Oh, and by the way, about the letter complaining about Paul eating on the coach, ignore it! I have told them you need to keep him

143

sweet in the morning. Try to encourage him to take a biscuit on board." She laughed. "Baked beans don't go down too well!"

I laughed too, bade her good-bye, and we parted company.

Chapter Twenty-eight

It was the first week in December and I could feel the pressure building up inside me. My head buzzed and I felt as though it would burst! Paul's behaviour carried on being unruly, and every day when I arrived at work I felt exhausted. I was jumpy and nervous and my hands were unsteady. I willed myself to cope with it and during the day, because I was kept busy, I gradually got better. By the end of the day I was tired, like anyone is, so the one redeeming feature was that after a busy day Paul was ready for bed. His breathing was still not stable enough, so the doctor had stepped up the nebulising to four times a day. This meant four hours on the machine each day, and although he was given one session at midday at school, and one from the home help at four o'clock, weekends were difficult. On Saturday I would come in at lunch-time and nebulise him and then Joe or Jeff would do it at four o'clock. I seemed to spend all Sunday doing it and trying to fit in my other jobs, but I felt more and more hopeless and helpless! Everything just seemed too much and I felt so sorry for Paul needing such constant medication. Sometimes the machine got a bit blocked and didn't work efficiently, and this caused me even more stress.

Suddenly, out of the blue, one Monday morning, Mrs Friston telephoned me at work.

"Is it OK to talk Mrs Carter?"

They all knew that I tried to keep my home life separate from the working one.

"Yes, I'm in my office," I said. I was trying to reconcile figures after Paul had given me a very turbulent hour before I got to work.

145

"I have spoken to the senior nursing officer at the Cedars and she has agreed that when Paul goes in next weekend for respite care he can stay," she paused. "They have taken him on the condition that you have him at home every other weekend."

I couldn't believe I was hearing this. I felt as if someone had relieved me of a great weight. My chest no longer felt tight with apprehension and worry. I could physically feel the tension easing inside me and relief coursing through my veins.

"You don't know how grateful I am Mrs Friston!"

My reply was a mild expression of how I felt.

She continued: "It's not an ideal placing for him, but it's all we can offer and it's a familiar place, so he won't have any trouble settling in."

I thanked her very much and she wished me well, and said she would keep in touch.

After I put the telephone down my thoughts were whirling. At last this was what I wanted and needed, what we all, as a family, needed! Now that the time had come I was not so sure. My conscience reared its ugly head. How would he get along without his family? How could I, as a mother, cast off my own son? And it suddenly struck me. He took up such a large part of my life. How would I manage without him? All day long these thoughts chased around inside my head.

When I went home at the end of the day, to my surprise, I found Jeff in bed. He was hot and feverish, and when I sympathetically stroked his forehead his weak voice informed me that he had 'flu. Poor Jeff, he was my number one person. I had always loved him above anyone else, so I had to find time to mother him a little. I asked Joe to bath Paul and get him ready for bed that night. "Dinner will be later. I want to make Dad comfortable."

Joe nodded agreement without moving his eyes away from the TV. Paul had dozed off on his bean bag.

I made Jeff some soup and took him some aspirins and water. I sat with him whilst he took them.

"Sorry you're ill, love. I'll telephone work in the morning and tell them you won't be in."

He nodded weakly. "I was supposed to be taking you to

146

the Christmas dinner on Friday whilst Paul's away."

I smiled. "You may be better by Friday. Let's wait and see." I made his pillows comfortable and put an extra blanket on the bed as he was shivering. He wanted to sleep so I left him to it. I could hear Paul chuckling with merriment and as I walked past the bathroom I saw Joe tipping a plastic beaker filled with warm water over Paul's tummy to his great amusement. Joe ruffled his hair, giving him such a fond look of affection that I could feel a lump in my throat, and the tears were pricking my eyes. I told myself not to be so damn stupid! We would still see him, but not as much, yet still my conscience persisted in troubling me.

Jeff slept most of Tuesday away, only waking up to take aspirins every so often. I came in from work at lunch-time and made him a cup of tea, and whilst I was there the telephone rang. I picked it up, wondering who it was likely to be when most people would expect the house to be empty.

"Hello, is that Mrs Carter? I'm afraid Paul is not well. Can you come and pick him up from school?"

This was all I needed, but I didn't really have a choice.

"Yes, OK. I'll come as soon as I can. Is he wheezy?"

"Yes, and his midday nebulising didn't seem to relieve him."

I felt the now all too familiar stab of fear inside, but tried to put things into order in my mind.

I put the telephone down and turned to Jeff. "Jeff, my love. I have to go and get Paul. He isn't well either."

"OK," he muttered sleepily.

This wasn't a new thing. It was part of our routine.

I telephoned the shop, saying I would be late back from lunch because my washing machine was leaking, and I told the staff to cope until I got back. I didn't like lying, but it was my way of keeping everything together, including my job.

Paul's school was only two miles away and the roads were empty. It was a grey miserable December day and not many cars were on the road. When I arrived he was lying on an air-bed in the classroom, his head propped up with cushions. I could hear his rapid breathing, but even in this uncomfortable state of distress, his eyes lit up and his face brightened

147

when he saw me.

"He brought his dinner up, Mrs Carter, and has been wheezy ever since."

"OK, I'll take him home to bed."

I thanked her and Paul got up slowly with difficulty.

"The car's outside, son." I told him encouragingly.

It would have been easy to sit him in a wheel-chair and take him out to the car. There would then be no risk of him biting me, but I felt that if I ever started that it would become a way of life. Maybe I'm crazy, but I wanted to try and help him to lead as normal a life as he possibly could. His teacher did not interfere, and as we walked with slow uneven steps I willed him to make it to the car. When we got there I laid him on the back seat, sighing with relief at his passiveness towards me. I put his head on the pillow that I had brought and then tucked a blanket round him. I decided to take him home and then see how his breathing was when we got there. I knew I must not panic.

I suddenly remembered his nebuliser, and as if reading my thoughts his teacher appeared with it. I thanked her.

"Poor Paul. I hope he's better for Christmas!"

"Yes, let's hope so!"

Chapter Twenty-nine

So far Paul had never had to spend Christmas in hospital. He spent Christmas Day with us and Boxing Day with Mark, so I was determined he would be well soon if I could do anything about it!

When I arrived home Paul seemed to be unable to stand up when it came to getting out of the car. I carried him, his feet dragging weakly along the ground, and thankfully we reached the inside of the house. I had felt the strain pulling on my back and I knew I would suffer for it tomorrow. I couldn't count the number of times I had damaged it over the years by trying to lift him. He stirred and woke up, making a supreme effort to walk as I puffed my way upstairs. Disturbing him had set the wheezing off again, so I put him on his nebuliser after making him comfortable in bed. I went in to see if Jeff was all right, and he was asleep. I then looked at Paul again and tossed up whether to call the doctor, but I could see that his colour was returning and his breathing stabilising. How could I go back to work and leave two invalids? I knew that Jeff would be all right, but he wouldn't be well enough to help Paul if he needed it. I took off my coat, intending to telephone and say that I couldn't come back today, and then I heard Jeff's voice.

"You're back. How is he?"

"He's in bed. I've just nebulised him."

He sat up gingerly looking pale and wan.

"I'm getting up to write a letter. I can watch him."

"Are you sure?" I was doubtful. It must have been an important letter, I thought. Jeff didn't usually write them when he was well. I did, and he just signed them!

He explained. "Yes, I'm sure. You know how busy you are at the shop. The directors won't appreciate you leaving it!"

I didn't protest too strongly. He was right. I hadn't yet told him Paul was going in to the Cedars to stay this weekend. Then I suddenly thought that if Paul had an infection, Mrs Marley, the senior nursing officer, would not take him until he was better. A selfish thought struck me. Maybe we would not be able to go out for our Christmas meal after all, even if Jeff was better. I felt ashamed of myself but nevertheless the thought was there.

I went back to work. Luckily I had only stretched thirty minutes over my lunch hour and I was soon caught up in the general rush of serving, and didn't have time to think of much else. I had only been back for about twenty minutes when Leslie appeared to help us cope with the long queue of customers lined along the shop with their goods clasped in their hands.

I didn't stop for a tea break, so was glad to close the door at the end of the day knowing I would be home soon. When I got in Jeff was sitting in his dressing gown watching TV. He looked a little better. He reminded me.

"You forgot to cancel Marie."

"Oh my God, yes!" She was our home help who cared for Paul until Jeff came home. Jeff laughed.

"She's glad you forgot. She said she likes coming and she's done the ironing. She told me to tell you that Paul is very thirsty."

"Did he keep drinks down? Oh good!"

I then proceeded to tell Jeff about the telephone call from Mrs Friston, and Paul's impending move to the Cedars. He visibly brightened, and I couldn't blame him for this. He had shared my attention for years. I added. "The only snag is if he isn't well he will have to go into hospital, and then Mrs Marley won't take him until he's better."

"We'll have to take that chance. We ought to let the doctor see him," was Jeff's reply.

I was in agreement with this and with Joe's help I took him in his pyjamas to evening surgery. Joe went off to pick up Amy from swimming, promising to collect us on the way back.

The doctor examined Paul while I explained the situation. "Normally I would say that hospital is the best place, but it doesn't appear to be an infection. It's his allergies again. I'm going to give him an injection, and as long as he improves in the next four hours you can keep him at home."

"Thank you so much, doctor."

"Well, we don't want to be stopped now that everyone has finally agreed about what's best for Paul and also for the rest of the family."

I held Paul with the help of the nurse whilst he had his injection, and within five minutes his breathing was easier. I thanked the doctor and we sat in the waiting room. Before long Joe arrived. Amy was in the car, complaining that she was hungry.

We drove home and I put Paul back to bed, content in the knowledge that he was getting better. I went through the motions of serving dinner, trying to analyse my emotions. I was relieved and sorry at the same time that he was going to the Cedars. Was there no pleasing me? I had to come to terms with the fact, finally, that I could not cope with him any more. I loved him dearly, as we all did, and this mental anguish tormented me.

When I went to bed that night I lay there next to Jeff, who was fast asleep. I could not contain my misery any longer and I sobbed myself to sleep. It wasn't just that night either. For a long time after that I cried myself into oblivion every night. It was something that I couldn't expect anyone else to understand, even Jeff, and although I knew it was for the best, and there could be no turning back now, the pain it caused me was immense.

When Friday came I arrived home from work feeling as though I didn't want to go out for a meal, but I said nothing. Paul's clothes were packed and I had bought him a new quilt. He had recovered from his wheezing, and was pleased to be going to the Cedars. I had planned to take him up there in the car myself, but Jeff reminded me that we had to meet at the restaurant at seven o'clock and I had barely half an hour to get ready.

"Joe will take him there for you."

"But I wanted to say good-bye!" I protested.

151

"It's not good-bye," said Jeff cheerfully. "He's coming home next weekend."

I only had time to give Paul a quick kiss before Joe whisked him off in the car and then I had to get ready for our evening out.

When we arrived at the restaurant we had to wait for half an hour before anyone else turned up. We sat there sipping a drink, and the peacefulness after such a hectic day was pleasant.

"Are you OK?" I enquired. He still looked tired.

"No, not really!" said Jeff, sounding very sorry for himself. I smiled inwardly. He had always been a baby where illness was concerned, but I knew if he was feeling that bad he wouldn't have gone out. He wasn't that noble!

The door opened and some of his colleagues came in. He was working in a new section so I didn't know any of them. He introduced me, and the other wives smiled in greeting. There was one female without a husband or boyfriend called Sheila. I could see from the onset that she had designs on Jeff. She sat herself opposite us, totally ignoring me and trying constantly to capture his attention. She had a face like a witch, with long straight hair, and she had applied her mascara to make her eyes look slanted. I felt nonplussed as she lightly tapped Jeff's arm. "Jeff, taste my wine, it's off and I want you to send it back."

I felt myself glaring at her. Who did she think she was giving my husband orders!

Jeff smiled sweetly, taking her proffered glass and slowly tasting it. He looked thoughtful and then picked up the bottle beside her, pouring me and himself a generous glassful. "Carrie, try this wine. Sheila doesn't like it, but I think you will. It's a sweet Bordeaux, our favourite!"

Sheila flung me a look of hate and hissed at Jeff. "I ordered dry white. I don't like sweet wine!"

Peter, the office manager, cut in wearily: "Come to the counter with me, Sheila, and choose another."

Sheila rose haughtily from her chair and directed her slanty eyes at him. He waited patiently for her and she moved slowly, making sure she had captured everyone's attention. It was short-lived. I thought to myself, as she rustled by in her long black skirt, that all she needed was a broomstick. I noticed the rumble of whispered annoyance as she disappeared.

"She's a pain! Why did she come?" asked Jeff jokingly, but yet I felt he meant it.

"You'd better come back soon, Jeff. She's been doing your work all week and it's gone to her head!" laughed Eric. Jeff laughed but I saw his look of annoyance, and I could see there was rivalry between them in their working life.

After that the evening passed pleasantly enough. I talked generally with the other wives, but we did not discuss our families in great depth. The meal was delicious and when we decided to make a move at about midnight, we said our good-byes and Joe arrived to drive us home. Jeff confessed to me that Sheila was the bane of his life, and was after his job.

"She likes you too!" I said, still feeling a little peeved.

"I tell you what, Carrie," he said, "I've tried to find her a broomstick to take off, but she won't go!"

We both laughed and he squeezed my hand. "I guess I'll have to stick with you, the lesser of the two evils!"

Marriage certainly released a husband from the need to pay his wife compliments, I thought ruefully, although I hadn't missed the meaning of his playful attempt to placate me. I wistfully thought of the days when he first knew me and had charmed his way into my heart, past all the barriers of my problems. As we turned into the drive I wondered if Paul was all right, and realised to my surprise that I had spent all the evening up until then without thinking about him.

"Jeff, did you really think we had to meet at seven?"

"Yes, love. I got the time wrong," he said quickly.

In retrospect, I think that he had deliberately hurried me out to avoid more anguish. Jeff was a man who could not put sympathy into words, but he knew me well, and his actions were proof of his sincerity. I silently thanked God for giving me this man who appeared to be so tough, but was really full of empathy!

153

Chapter Thirty

In the beginning Paul appeared to settle in very well at the Cedars. His breathing improved, and his nebulising was cut down to twice a day. I called in to see him for half an hour twice a week on the way home from work and he came home every other weekend. It was lovely for me. After over twenty years of bringing up children I had time to spare for everyone and even a little for myself.

Christmas 1987 came and went. Annette came home for a visit and returned to America in the new year full of excitement. She had achieved her aim. She had been spotted whilst competing and had been offered a scholarship. It was a four year course with a degree at the end of it for PE. We were very proud of her. She had won herself quite a few medals and trophies. Now she was going back to get on with it. She had matured considerably after being away from home for a year and I could see her new life now taking shape for her.

1988 arrived, and now my pace of life was more tolerable. Joe was doing well at his job as a silk screen printer, and Amy was doing well at school and swimming and was set to swim in the nationals again this year. In August Jeff and I went to see her swim in the 200 metres breaststroke and to our delight and frustration she ended up as first reserve for the final. So near and yet so far! This added to her determination to do even better next year.

There was a niggling doubt about Paul in my mind and it plagued me constantly. I could see that he was regressing in some things at the Cedars. Dr Bass had been right. Most of the residents were physically and mentally handicapped there

154

and had to spend their life in a wheel-chair. They could not feed themselves and although Paul could, he was now loth to. He could see others being helped and thought he was missing out. His table manners were no longer acceptable, and he made a terrible mess when he ate his food. But the worst thing of all was that he had watched the other residents being wheeled out to have their bath, and when he was called one evening whilst I was there, to my absolute horror and amazement he sat himself in a spare wheel-chair and like lightning propelled it to the nearest bathroom. I'm sure he would have been the victor in a disabled olympics competition, as he manoeuvred it at high speed with such dexterity. I heard a chuckle from the nurse in the bathroom, but after all the years of not giving in to that I did not find it funny. I followed him.

"Can't you stop him from doing that? He can use his legs." I enquired.

"It's only because he sees the others. He knows he can walk," she said defensively. Paul gave his impish grin.

"Use your legs, Paul!" I told him sternly.

I did not blame the nurses. The hospital was so under-staffed, and I had been lucky that they had agreed to take him. I knew now that my stamina was running down. Coping with him every other weekend was as much as I could manage now, and I really did hate to see him regressing and becoming institutionalised after all the years of family life, but I didn't know what the answer was.

Autumn came and went and before I knew it we were working extra time at work for Christmas. On one particular morning I was sitting in my office having my coffee and the telephone rang. I ignored it initially, as it was my break time, but someone called out to tell me it was for me. It was the manager of another branch.

"Hello, Carrie. We've had a call for you. Your line was engaged. It was Mrs Marley from the Cedars."

I stiffened. What could be wrong?

She went on. "She said you are used to your son having asthma attacks and not to panic. Unfortunately they've had to take him to the hospital, as the facilities at the Cedars are not suitable, and you can ring up later to see how he is."

"I see." I relaxed a little. "Did she say if it was a bad attack?"

"No. She just said 'phone up later."

I thanked her and put the telephone down. Already my problems, so well concealed for years, were getting known around the company. The telephone rang again. This time I picked it up. It was Jerry, one or our directors from head office. News about it had reached there already and all this was winding me up.

"Will you need some relief help so that you can leave the shop? I hear you have a family crisis," he said kindly.

I tried to stay calm. I should be used to it after all these years. "The message I have is to ring later, but I will go through and enquire. If I need to leave the shop I will tell you."

He seemed satisfied. "OK, I'll get off the line so that you can use it."

I said good-bye and cleared down. When I telephoned the hospital I realised I hadn't asked what ward he was in, so I explained this to the switchboard operator. She managed to sort out his whereabouts pretty quickly, to my surprise, and the telephone was answered by a staff nurse.

"I'm telephoning to enquire about my son, Paul Benson. He has just been admitted."

"One moment please."

She was gone, obviously to see how he was faring. When she came back to the telephone she spoke slowly and carefully. "We have no news for you at the moment. Please 'phone back in an hour."

That was a little odd! I presumed that they were waiting for the doctor to see him and then maybe release him or keep him in. I asked again. "Would it be all right if I came to see him?"

She said with great deliberation, "There is no point at the moment, but we'll know in an hour."

Oh well, it seemed that there wasn't much to worry about. They were obviously trying to stop me from dashing down there and then finding he had been taken back to the Cedars.

I still felt uneasy and kept glancing at my watch wishing that hour would pass. In the meantime, Leslie had arrived, ready to give us some help in the shop. He kept glancing at me, but said nothing, and after an hour I went to use the telephone again. Oh what a pain, someone was on it with a lengthy order! She saw my movement and tried to finish quickly, grimacing as she put it down.

"Why does everything happen at once?" she grumbled. "Sorry to keep you waiting."

Her words were going over my head, and I nodded agreement whilst dialling the hospital number, remembering to ask for the ward this time. I was put through to the same staff nurse. I repeated my enquiry about Paul. Her voice was brisker.

"You can talk to the doctor now, Mrs Carter."

Oh, so they were going to discharge him. The doctor's voice came over the line. "Hello, Mrs Carter. Paul is out of danger now. We think he will pull through."

What! Disbelief flooded through me. "Out of danger!" I repeated. My God! Surely he hadn't been that bad. I wasn't even there. I felt dizzy and sick with shock. My voice was weak and quavery. This shock had drained me. "I didn't know he was in danger. No one said! Oh my God, I feel so bad! I should have come!"

His voice was kindly. "There was nothing you could have done. Now is the time to come. He needs you to be there when he wakes up, but don't be concerned when you see all the tubes."

My God, I really was frightened now! I asked myself what sort of mother was I? For years I had dropped everything to take him to hospital when necessary, but this time, when he needed me most of all, I had failed to realise he was so ill! I was shaking and I babbled out some sort of explanation to Leslie. I don't even know what I said!

"Just go! And drive carefully," he said. "I will stay here in your place."

I didn't need a second bidding. I paused only to ring Jeff, but I played down the seriousness of it over the telephone. I could tell him details later. I ran out to my car, not seeing anyone as I passed through the shop. I was almost hysterical, but I knew I must get myself together. I was no good to Paul like this. I prayed to God so many times to let him live!

157

When I arrived at the hospital I was directed to a separate room, next to the men's ward. As I went in the sister said brightly. "You must be Paul's mum. I can see the likeness."

I was not interested in preliminaries. "Please can I see him? How is he?"

"Much better!" And she guided me over to his bed. I couldn't believe what I saw!

Paul lay there, his skin had a delicate cream-like appearance. His eyes were closed, and he had an oxygen mask over his face, pumping air through his half open lips. His arm had a drip flowing in to his vein and there seemed to be tubes everywhere. Nearby there was a machine monitoring his heart. I could see the zig-zag line forming on the screen. Looking at all this made me realise that my son was very ill! Sister met my horrified gaze.

"He's over the worst. At the moment he is still unconscious, but his heart beat is strong. Don't be put off by all the equipment. It's helping him to recover."

I didn't utter a word. I couldn't. I just drew up a chair and sat, stroking his limp little wrist. His eyes fluttered open briefly, and then I noticed a change in sister's composure.

"Oh Paul, you're going to be all right! You knew your mum was here." She turned to me saying, "I don't like worrying times like that."

I couldn't cuddle him or get near because of all the tubes, but I lay, my head against his hand, and sobbed with relief that once again he had cheated death!

Chapter Thirty-one

I sat with Paul for three hours and during that time he improved dramatically. After half an hour the doctor came and he removed the heart monitor and the oxygen mask. Paul slowly recovered consciousness, and the smile that he gave me, although weak and wan, was a tonic. It brought tears of relief to my eyes. After two hours the tubes were removed, but he was kept on the drip because as yet he couldn't eat and the glucose would help to sustain some energy. At the end of three hours the doctor gently suggested that I return to work. He said I would not need to worry about him and I could return again in the evening. I went reluctantly, but I knew it made sense. I had another life as well, and a family. I was still confused as to why it had been such a bad attack. He had never needed that sort of treatment before and the doctor said he didn't know either. My God, I couldn't bear the thought of it happening again! How frightened he must have been, and never being able to tell anyone he felt ill. Could any of us imagine the mental anguish and feelings of isolation, locked in his own little world and totally unable to break out of it and help himself by speaking!

I went back to work and finished out the day. Leslie told me I could go home but I needed to keep my mind occupied. When I went home and told the family how bad it had been they were all very shocked and wanted to come to the hospital too, so we all ended up going to see Paul that evening. I was amazed when I saw Paul. He was sitting up in bed, smiling. The smile that never fails to capture my heart. It was hard to believe that less than eight hours before he had almost died.

159

Sister said very proudly, "Paul is the bravest young man I have ever seen, Mrs Carter! His will to live is so strong! He is determined to get better soon, and he will. The right attitude is the secret of success."

I felt admiration for him too. "Yes, he's had so many things against him from the day he was born. It doesn't seem fair to me but he's a fighter!"

As I looked at Paul, excitedly waving his arms at us, while Joe and Amy helped him to play with his cars, it suddenly struck me that in spite of all the illnesses and adversities he really loved his life. It made me wonder just what right we mothers have to decide whether a handicapped foetus should be aborted before birth. I knew that if Paul had been asked he would say emphatically, "My life is worth living!"

That same evening Paul was able to eat a little soup and drink fruit juice. His quick recovery was nothing short of a miracle and by the next day he was back on solid food again. On the third day he was discharged and I drove him back to the Cedars, and stayed to put him to bed and make him comfortable.

We had been given an appointment to see his paediatrician in three weeks, which was just after Christmas, and on a cold day in late December we returned to see him in out-patients.

Mr Kiro, his Japanese paediatrician seemed pleased to see us. He gave Paul a car to hold whilst he examined him, and then pronounced his lungs clear. I could see, when he sat down again at his desk, that Mr Kiro was in a state of agitation. He had a habit of giggling at the end of each sentence so I never really knew how seriously to take him, but what he had to say was no laughing matter!

"Paul has recovered well, but the doctor at the Cedars nearly killed him!" My gaze was riveted on him. Whatever did he mean?

"I don't understand Mr Kiro."

"Paul has been coming in here for quite a few years now, mainly to give you a break when he's ill. He has never given us cause for alarm until then! Unfortunately I was on holiday and didn't hear about it until after, but *that* doctor," he stabbed his finger at an imaginary mark on his notebook, "gave Paul an injection that nearly killed him. How he

survived the massive allergic reaction we really don't know!"
He was angry now and so was I.

"But I have to trust all the doctors that care for Paul. I
know nothing!"

"He had no right. He overstepped his mark. As Paul's
doctor I could have told him it would be dangerous. I am
sending over written instructions that they must *never*
do it again! Next time he might not be so lucky."

Paul sat there unconcerned as we discussed him, but
my immediate concern was for his safety.

"Please, Mr Kiro, do! I need to know that no mistakes
will be made again!" My tone was urgent. This was enough
to destroy all faith in human nature. After all, if the doctors
didn't know, who else was there?"

They were supposed to be trained in healing the sick, not
killing them! Once again he assured me that Paul would not
be put at risk and we took our leave. Obviously it made me
lose a little faith in the Cedars, but it wasn't the hospital
or the staff, just one doctor. If I'm fair about it, everyone
in life makes mistakes, no one is perfect, but human error
when it involves one's life is a very serious matter.

When I asked Melissa, the staff nurse who supervised Paul's
care most of the time, about it, she was very non-committal,
insisting that the doctor had done his best to help Paul, and
she wasn't aware that he would have had a bad reaction to an
injection. Whether I should have pursued the matter any
further I really don't know, but I wasn't after getting anyone
into trouble, only reassurance that Paul would always be in
safe hands when he was ill.

After this crisis had passed we settled back into our usual
routine and in the new year Annette came back for a visit.
She brought Tim, her new boyfriend, with her. He was an
American navy pilot and on the eve of her birthday he asked
our permission to marry her. We willingly gave it, and they
became engaged. We were charmed by his old-fashioned
courtesy. My only misgiving was their plans to live in
America. Still, it was Annette's life, and I knew I would just
have to adjust to not seeing her very often.

Paul's face lit up as soon as he saw her. He had not forgotten his sister, and I warmed to Tim because Paul liked

him. He insisted on holding Tim's arm everywhere he went. I remarked. "Anyone would think that Tim was your brother, Paul!"

Maybe Paul was showing us his acceptance of Tim as a new member of our family.

The winter passed and the spring of 1989 came. There were three important happenings that year. Firstly, in June Paul had his eighteenth birthday. We bought him a cake in the shape of a car. He had three parties, one at the Cedars, one with us, to which my dad, my brother, Rob and Bessie, my stepmother, came, and one with Mark and his girlfriend Jean. We were lucky on the day that he came to us. The weather was so beautiful that we were able to have a barbecue in the garden. Paul loved the simple things in life and could hardly contain his excitement when he had his barbecued sausages with rolls and salad. He followed it with jelly and ice-cream. His face was alight with pleasure at this simple little event, and I thought reflectively how much more lovable and easier to cope with he was now that the aggressiveness towards us had diminished. What I didn't know was that he was well behaved at home but at the Cedars he wasn't.

The second important event was the nationals, and this time Amy really excelled herself. She finished fourth in the 100 metres breaststroke. Fourth in the whole of Great Britain was no mean achievement! She was also part of the relay team that once again won the gold. This gave a tremendous fillip and we relived these exciting events in our minds for years afterwards.

This was just as well because now we only have memories. After this, in spite of our encouragement, and that of her coach, who was convinced that she could make the Esso Youth Squad, Amy decided to retire from competitive swimming. She had never been an organised person and she wanted to pass her GCSEs. Swimming training dominated her life, and she found it impossible to combine the two. She had amassed a room full of trophies and medals over the past seven years, represented her county on numerous occasions and swam in a team for Great Britain twice. We were devastated but we had to remember it was her life, and only she could live it.

The third exciting happening was Annette and Tim's marriage. The wedding was to be in New York. My first reaction was of horror! I was terrified of flying! Flights on package tours to Spain in 1970 had developed my fear and I had evaded doing it ever since. However, I knew I would have to fight it. There was no way that I would miss this wedding. Amy was going to be a bridesmaid. She had a lovely cornflower blue dress with blue shoes and was very excited about it. The only thing that gave me a little pang was the knowledge that Paul could not come. Even if I could have been sure that his behaviour would be acceptable I had no way of knowing if flying and the change of environment, would upset his asthma. It was a risk I could not take so he had to stay at home.

We were away for five days. The day of the wedding was warm and sunny. The chapel was set on a hill overlooking the bay and as Tim was in the navy the ceremony was conducted in the Academy Chapel. As they came out to pass through the avenue of crossed swords, as in military weddings, the look of happiness on Annette's face made me feel so happy for her.

When we came home, complete with photographs and a video, it felt quite flat going back to work. But on my first morning back I received a telephone call from Mrs Friston. I told her excitedly about the wedding and she expressed her good wishes to them. I suddenly felt a bit guilty about Paul.

"I'm going to the Cedars straight from work to see Paul tonight. After all I haven't seen him for five days!"

"That's what I'm 'phoning about."

A thought struck me. "He is OK?" Oh God, please don't let him be ill!

"Yes, he's very well."

I relaxed, but her tone became mysterious.

"Can you go and see Dr Bass tomorrow at two o'clock? She wants to discuss Paul with you."

"Yes, of course."

I often took my lunch hour then. The interviews usually only took about half an hour. I put the telephone down wondering what fate had in store for me now!

163

Chapter Thirty-two

I stopped in at the Cedars to see Paul after work. He was hyperactive, not sitting still at all, just constantly moving from one spot to another. As usual there were few nurses in sight. It was very understaffed but at least they didn't have the problem of Paul raiding the fridge or food cupboard, as at home. When the meals were ready they were wheeled in on a trolley. I stayed until his bath time and then went home to organise dinner. I told Jeff about my appointment the next day. He was cautious, not prepared to comment. "Wait until you see Dr Bass."

This did not stop me from speculating. Somehow I knew that something was not right, and I dreaded hearing any more bad news. I was sad that Paul had regressed at the Cedars and was not getting the mental stimulation that he desperately needed, but I had experienced two years of help from all the stress, more freedom to do things, and I knew as far as having him to live permanently at home I had come to the end of the line. Mentally and physically, even with the help of my family, I could no longer cope with it!

When I arrived for my appointment with Dr Bass, I was not kept waiting for long. The buzzer sounded and I smiled my thanks to the receptionist. She asked. "Do you know the way to Dr Bass's office?"

"Yes, thank you."

I climbed the stairs and walked along the corridor. I knocked tentatively on the door and it was opened by Dr Bass, smiling and welcome. "Please come in Mrs Carter, and sit down."

I perched nervously on the edge of the chair as she took

her seat behind the desk. As ever she was brisk and to the point. "We have to do something about Paul. They are refusing to have him any more at the Cedars!"

"What! This is the first I knew! I was up there yesterday and nothing was said to me."

"Staff are not allowed to say anything, but he's just too lively. He throws things around when he feels like it and bites chunks out of people at any time. Someone with behavioural problems like that should not be with people in wheel-chairs. It's not fair on them!"

I was silent. What could I say? I knew Paul could be frightening to able bodied people when angry, but I hadn't realised that it was still going on. I had been lulled into a false sense of security because he had been so good on his recent visits home. She continued.

"Paul doesn't fall into any particular category. He's not a mongol, and although there are autistic tendencies, he is not classed as fully autistic, otherwise he would have been referred to a residential school years ago."

What she was saying was that everyone was passing the buck, I felt. No one wanted to say that he would fit in to a particular group of mental handicap. Yet he had been at school with other handicapped children of mixed ability for years. She hadn't finished yet.

"Another problem is that he is getting bored with going to school. In the morning he fakes wheeziness when the coach is due. After it has gone he makes a miraculous recovery, and then spends all day being bored and driving the nurses mad."

I sighed and my heart felt heavy with sadness. My poor little misfit. Did no one want him?

"We have a solution if you will agree."

Hope flooded through my heart. I had known for a while that the Cedars was only a temporary answer to the problem. I listened with nervous anticipation.

"There are no placings in the local area that could benefit Paul, but we have a married couple who live at Hastings."

She saw my face change because it was about sixty-five miles away from us. She went on to explain that they worked at a residential home for handicapped people, in fact had done for over eight years. Now they wanted to start a smaller unit in their own home to provide a family atmosphere. They were intending to take Paul if we agreed, and two others later, all with behavioural problems.

"Could he be attacked by the others?" I asked nervously. The fact that Paul was aggressive made me worry that he might receive more violence than he could cope with.

"No! They will be supervised on a one to one basis."

I could see that there wasn't really a choice. I could no longer cope with Paul and neither could the Cedars. However, if he was sixty-five miles away, the most I could hope to see him would be about once a month. Dr Bass added something else that hadn't yet occurred to me.

"It's possible that the sea air will help his chest, and there may be fewer asthma attacks."

Now that was a comforting thought. Suddenly the idea became more appealing. I would make myself cope with the separation. I could put up with anything if I thought that Paul's health would improve.

"Would you like to go down, take Paul and meet this couple? I think you will like them."

"Yes, please. Jeff would come too, I know."

So it was arranged for the next evening. Mark was also going to pay a visit, but later on in the week, when he wasn't so busy. Joe drove us down there, and Melissa, the staff nurse from the Cedars, came too. She felt as guilty as I did in admitting that she had come to the end of the line with coping with Paul, but like us she wanted to be sure in her own mind that he would be going somewhere that he would be happy to live.

When we arrived Ted and Sally introduced themselves at the door. "Come on in. I expect you would like a cup of tea."

Jeff's eyes lit up at the mention of his favourite beverage, and Paul gave a whoop of joy when he saw the food spread out on the table. This was completely unexpected, but as we had driven down straight after work it was very welcome. To my amazement Paul tucked into crusty bread and salad, something I never usually gave him because he made such a mess. But today he was on his best behaviour. It was almost as if he knew it would be to his benefit.

Ted and Sally spoke about their future plans and I was impressed by their sincerity and earnestness. They explained that having worked with people who had become institutionalised had made them want to offer a home and family life. I knew that this was what Paul needed. After all, it was the way he had spent the first sixteen years of his life. We were shown the room that was to be Paul's bedroom, and the baby alarm system so that any distress with breathing could be acted on straight away. They explained that there was a day centre within walking distance where Paul would go during the day. In the afternoon outings were provided and swimming, bowling and other recreational pursuits also. This was more than we could have hoped to provide him with at home, and coupled with such a caring attitude it was more than we could have ever dreamed of. One thought occurred to me as I looked over at my smiling charming son, who was heartily attacking a bowl of jelly and ice-cream. Tonight the world was his oyster!

"You do know that Paul has behavioural problems. He can be moody and aggressive, and the nebulising makes life very restricted for him."

"Don't worry," said Sally. "I have a brother with asthma and I'm used to it. The aggression is something that we will learn to weather and eventually minimise."

I felt satisfied that this would be good for Paul, but I wanted to discuss it with Jeff at home. All the advantages were there, and the only disadvantage was the fact that he was a further distance away from us. I knew that if it was best for Paul I could get used to it. As we were driven home we discussed it, Jeff was in favour and so was I. Joe also added his endorsement of the idea. All we needed now was Mark to agree, after he had been down.

Three days later, having heard from Mark, too, our minds were made up. I telephoned Dr Bass and told her of our decision. "Yes, we agree to let Paul go to Hastings."

She was delighted and relieved. Pressures had been put on her from the Cedars to do something and this was the solution.

"You won't regret it! I shall review his progress every three months and I'm confident that there will be an improvement in health and behaviour."

I thanked her for all her help and kindness and put the telephone down. We had made plans to move Paul down there the following weekend. A week after that he would be home for Christmas so this would help him to get used to the change gradually. So the next weekend found us moving Paul and all his belongings, complete with his box of cars and his teddy-bear, to his new home. Once again I felt the all too familiar lump in my throat and a feeling of conscience for agreeing to send him away. But this time overriding all this was a feeling that this could be the beginning of new and better opportunities for Paul.

EPILOGUE

Today is Paul's twenty-first birthday. The weather is kind to us and we are sitting in the garden having a barbecue. This is one of the things he enjoys the most. As I look over at Jeff his glass of wine raised as he chats to my dad, I think of all that has happened in the last three years.

Ted and Sally now have two little daughters, one aged two years and the other has just celebrated her first birthday. I'm told that Paul is very gentle with them and he is allowed to hold them on his lap at times. There are also two other young adults living with them as well. Paul was given six months to settle down and after that Roy and Rex came. They are three years older than Paul, autistic, but able to speak. They are all close, like brothers, and the other two understand Paul's needs very well and convey them verbally for him.

His life is full. He goes to the day centre and works at producing pictures and models which are sold at craft fairs. Coach outings, excursions to the theatre, long walks and trips to the beach are all normal occurrences. His table manners are much improved. So, too, are his behaviour problems. His tempers are rare and usually only occur when something changes and he becomes confused. He never has tantrums at home now and we are able to have him to stay once a month for the weekend, and at Christmas and Easter. I still have to keep an eye on him when he makes sandwiches, or raids the fridge. One day Jeff may remember to put a lock on it for me!

His health is much better. He has only been in hospital once in the last three years. His fits are rare, three in three years, and he only needs the nebuliser twice a day now.

169

He makes his contribution to household tasks, unwilling though it may be! He dries up dishes, and if he can run and hide after a meal to avoid it he will. He makes his bed with such enthusiasm when he comes to stay that I usually find he has changed his sheets every night!

Paul is an uncle now. Annette had a little girl, Ruth, in 1990. Paul was able to see her when they came to stay when Ruth was a year old. We visited Paul and took him out for lunch at McDonald's. This seemed to go down well with Paul and Ruth.

I feel more in control of my life now. Jeff and I are enjoying these golden years together. He certainly deserves it! He waited patiently for a long time without resentment or signs of anger for me to have time for him, and I will always love and admire him deeply for that. I never think too hard about how long Paul's life will be. All I content myself with is the fact that the quality of it is so much better for him now. I am left with this feeling of deep admiration for my son who has been so brave. He has fought illness and adversity since the day he was born, and survived! Let it be a lesson to the rest of us when we complain about the trivial things in life. If we have good health it should never be taken for granted. The experience of bringing up Paul has been a mixture of happiness, sadness, stress and discord, but there have also been many humorous occasions, too, as there can be with all children. I know as a family it has made the bonds of love stronger, and I hope as people it has made us less selfish, more patient, and more appreciative of life. I know if I had this time again I would help Paul with his fight to survive. He loves life and wants to live so much!

Jeff is raising his glass. "Carrie, this is to Paul, twenty-one years old, congratulations!"

I look at my son, happiness written all over his face. He has spotted the ice-cream! I raise my glass. Joe ruffles his hair, and he allows Amy to hug him, briefly.

"Happy birthday, Paul! Yes you can have ice-cream!"

He laughs merrily, and his eyes meet mine, briefly. He gives me that special look that I like to think is especially reserved for Mum.

"I love you, Paul!"